Going to the Dogs

by
Ian McCormack

Published by: Carel Press Ltd, 4 Hewson Street, Carlisle, CA2 5AU
Tel 01228 538928
Email Carel_Press@compuserve.com
Web http://ourworld.compuserve.com/homepages/Carel_Press

First published 2000

Cover photograph: Howard Barlow
Cover design: Arthur Proctor

PERFORMANCE

For permission to give a public performance of any of these plays, please write to
Carel Press. No fee will be charged for a performance in an educational, charitable or
youth institution unless an admission charge is made, however, permission is still
required.

Printed by MFP, Manchester

ENVIRONMENTAL INFORMATION

The book is printed on 100% recycled paper which is made entirely from printed
waste, and is not re-bleached. Using recycled paper saves trees, water and energy, and
reduces air pollution and landfill.

British Library Cataloguing in Publication Data
McCormack, Ian
Going to the Dogs: a play about truanting
1. Title 11. Series
ISBN 1872365 64 7

The Characters

Caroline's family

| Caroline Dearman | Mr John Dearman | Mrs Pat Dearman |

Her friends

| Jo | Jake | Paul | Lucy | Tom |
| Mike | 'Big' Lowther | Laura | John | Karen |

The gang

| Tony | Shelley | Piggy | Ingrid | Bazzer |

The teachers

Miss Butterlee	Mr Marsh	Mrs Ratcliffe
Mr Hartson	French Teacher	Geography Teacher
RE Teacher	Miss Murgatroyd	Mrs Nevins

Other Adults

| Jessie | Mr Wardle | Customer |

As will be seen from the original cast list on pages 87-88, it is possible to change the gender of some parts and to add other parts.

ACT 1

Scene 1 — In the Park

It is the summer holidays. A group of children, boys and girls, who will start secondary school in September have just finished playing rounders. There is discussion of the game as they sink onto the grass and begin to drink from the bottles that they carry with them. Throughout the following exchange, it is obvious from the side of the argument they support, which team the respective children have played on.

Jake: I still say I was in.

Jo: Shut up Jake and give us a drink.

Mike: He's right though.

Jo: Give us a drink.

Jake: And if I'm right ...?

Lucy: Which he is ...

Jake: Then I'm still in.

Tom: And that was a rounder.

Jo: *(Becoming impatient)* Give us a drink.

Jake: So we're level.

Tom: And we've got two more batters left ...

Mike: Three with Jake ...

Jake: So we've actually won, not lost ...

Jo: OK you've won. *(She makes a grab for the bottle)* Now give us a drink.

Jake: *(Holding on tight)* Not till you tell everybody. Shout it!

Jo: I want a drink and Jake's team won!

There is widespread reaction to Jo's statement, protests on the one hand and cheers on the other. As the dialogue continues, it is drowned out by a variety of smaller but vigorous arguments between various team members.

Jake: *(Still holding on)* Say it again.

Jo: I've said it once, give us a drink.

Paul: She can't say it because you lost.

Mike: We didn't.

Paul: You know you did, so just give her a drink.

Jo and Jake begin wrestling with the bottle and the argument descends into chaos. After a moment Caroline intervenes.

Caroline: Shut up everyone. *(The group begins to respond, but only slowly)* Shut up, it's Lowther's brother.

The group becomes more subdued and begins to look for 'Big' Lowther.

Tom: Where?

Caroline: Over there by the swings.

Jake: He's coming this way.

Jo: Hide the ball!

Mike: I wonder what he wants.

Paul: You going to ask him?

Paul doesn't get an answer and the group sit in silence as Big Lowther approaches.

Big Lowther: Hello you lot, you seen our Dek?

Jake: We've not seen him all day. We've been playing rounders.

During this next exchange, Big Lowther helps himself to Jake's drink. There is no resistance and it is clear from the reactions of the others that no-one is at ease in his presence.

Big Lowther: Rounders, that's nice *(pause)* for babies. You wait until September, I'll show you some really grown up games when you get to our school.

He bends down and takes the ball from Jo's hand. He looks at it for a moment and then throws it as far away as he can. Laughing to himself he walks away without saying another word, still drinking from Jake's bottle of pop. There is a short silence before anyone speaks.

5

Caroline: Well done Jo.

Jo: What have I done?

Caroline: You've upset him, that's what!

Jo: I never.

Caroline: You did, holding on to the ball like that. You upset him.

Jo: I never, and anyway what difference does it make?

Caroline: He'll get us won't he? Next term when we start High School, he'll get us.

Jo: I wish you'd stop going on. Nobody will get us. It's just stories.

Caroline: So Adrian Mannion never got his head flushed down the toilet then?

Jo: It doesn't happen.

Mike: It does. Our kid told us, and they throw you in the brook.

Jake: Your kid would tell you anything. He hates you since you told on him and Sarah Potter.

Mike: Well, they kicked me out of the lounge.

Jake: You were hiding behind the couch ...

Paul: With a Polaroid camera ...

Jo: And a tape recorder.

Mike: They were supposed to be baby-sitting. I was collecting evidence.

Lucy: Pervert.

Tom: Andrew Hardy says that if they don't like you they burn your PE kit and they cut your hair off.

Jo: *(With mock seriousness)* And they steal your bike and they machine gun your parents. Oh, and if you tell anyone they cut off your legs with broken glass.

Everyone is laughing.

Caroline: It's not funny Jo. *(To everyone)* They do get you and you can't tell the teachers.

Jo: Caroline, it's not going to happen, and even if it was, there's nothing you can do about it.

Lucy: We don't even start there for three weeks.

Paul: Can't we just find the ball and finish the game?

The group disperses, speculating on the whereabouts of the ball and resuming their earlier argument about who is in etc. Caroline stands alone centre stage as the others leave. Jo turns back.

Jo: Are you coming Caz, or what?

Caroline: In a minute maybe, you go on.

Jo shrugs and exits, leaving Caroline very much alone. The lights fade to blackout.

Scene 2 – Caroline's House

Caroline's parents, John and Pat are in the living room. The house is modern and the room contains easy chairs and a table as well as the type of television, fireplace etc which one might expect to find in a comfortable family home. The Dearmans are not especially wealthy but they both work in well paid jobs, John in insurance and Pat in a management position with a Building Society. John is sitting in an armchair completing the crossword in one of the broadsheet daily newspapers. Pat is arranging flowers at the table and as she cuts the stems etc. she hums along to a piece of light classical music which is playing rather loudly.

Mum: *(Shouting to someone offstage)* Come on then, let's have a look at you. *(She waits for a response, though none comes)* Turn that thing down, John.

He does so.

Caroline, come down. Let's have a look at you.

There is a pause and Caroline enters the room resplendent in her new school uniform. Even the labels are still attached.

Oh Caroline, you look lovely, *(pause)* doesn't she John? Doesn't she look a picture?

7

Caroline:

Dad: *(Without looking)* Yes darling, splendid.

Caroline: He's not even looking.

Mum: *(Admonishing)* John, you could at least look.

Dad: What? *(Pause)* Oh yes, *(he looks)* very nice, very nice indeed.

Pat crosses to Caroline and begins to straighten her tie, tug at her collar etc.

Mum: You don't think the cardigan's too big do you?

Dad: No love, it's fine.

Mum: I can change it.

Dad: It's fine.

Mum: And the shirts, I got them a bit bigger on purpose. *(To Caroline)* You like them baggy, don't you love?

She adjusts the shirt, tucking it further into the skirt.

Caroline: *(Who is by now tired of being a 'shop dummy')* Mum, get off will you! I don't want it like that.

Mum: It looks messy the other way love and anyway, you don't want to get into trouble

Caroline: Mum, it looks stupid your way, I'm not a baby you know.

Dad: And you're not on a fashion parade either. You don't get grade A's by being trendy you know. It's results that count from now on, not playing games, like at junior school.

Caroline: Dad, I've not even started there yet!

Dad: Never mind that. You start as you mean to go on. If you want a job then you have to do well these days. If you won't take your chances then someone else will. So you can forget all this being trendy with your mates. It's work we want from you my girl.

Caroline: Dad, it's not fair! I just wanted my shirt out a bit. Everyone has it like that.

Dad: Well, you're not everyone, you're my daughter. I expect you to look respectable.

Caroline: Look like an idiot, more like.

Mum: Caroline! Don't talk to your father like that.

Caroline: That's right! Take his side! Never mind how stupid I look.

Mum: It's not a question of sides, Caroline. We want you to do well. I've told you before we've got high hopes for you.

Caroline: Well I don't want you to have anything for me. I'm not a performing dog, I'm just ordinary so leave me alone.

Dad: Now look here Caroline, I won't have you ...

Caroline: I'm not listening.

Mum: Caroline ...

Caroline: I hate you two and I hate this house. You're supposed to enjoy school you know.

She storms out of the room as she says this and runs upstairs. John and Pat are left looking stunned for a moment before the lights cut to blackout.

Scene 3 – The Park Playground

The children from the first scene are together again but this time they are lounging about the playground on benches, swings etc.

Tom: I had to get my pants from the Co-op. *(There is general astonishment)* I mean, can you imagine? Pants from the Co-op?

Paul: That's stupid. You can get grey pants anywhere.

Tom: I know that, but my mum says you get better quality from the Co-op and they're on the school's official list.

Lucy: My mum came back from Marks and Sparks with a **pleated** skirt.

Jo: What did you do?

Lucy: Made her take it back. I mean. *(Sarcastic)* Yes mother, I really am going to wear that – it was massive, nearly down to my ankles.

Jake: My mum just gave me the money, last Tuesday. I got it all: shirts, blazer, everything.

Mike: That's rubbish that, because I saw you last Tuesday and your mum was with you.

The others laugh at him.

Jake: Alright, she came with me but she let me choose everything.

Tom: Where did you go?

Jake: I got my pants on the market, you know, that fat guy with the beard.

Tom: I wanted to go there.

Paul: My mum says the Indian bloke has better stuff. That's where I got mine.

Caroline: I had to try mine on the other day while my dad gave me a lecture on education in the middle ages.

Jo: My mum took a picture of me. It's going to look stupid. She made me pull my socks right up and leave all the labels on in case anything had to go back.

Lucy: That's nothing, Paul Minshull's been out in his.

Paul: What, in the garden like?

Lucy: No, OUT! Out with his mum and dad.

The gang is astonished and all speak at once.

All: Never / You're joking / Get lost etc.

Paul: Where did he go?

Lucy: *(Pauses for full dramatic effect)* Are you ready for this?

They all nod.

Are you sure?

They all nod again.

Are you certain?

They nod a third time.

He went ... to his cousin's ... WEDDING!

They all scream and shout as if poisoned or in some pain. They all speak at once.

All: Can you imagine? / In public? / Everyone there? / A wedding? etc.

It fades to quiet.

Jake: There you are then. It proves it.

Paul: What?

Jake: They're mad, all of the Minshulls, his mum, dad, everybody. They're all barmy.

Lucy: They're not.

Jake: They are. His mum goes shopping in wellies.

Lucy: So what, I've been shopping in wellies.

Jake: In June?

Mike: Perhaps they haven't got much money.

Tom: They're loaded. His dad's got his own business.

Paul: They've got a dead big house.

Lucy: That's true. And his sister's got a horse.

Tom: That's it then, rich but mad.

Jake: Hey, do you remember that time James came to school with his hair all sticking up cos his mum had cut it for him?

Paul: What about his brother, Norman? She dyed his.

Mike: Turned out orange.

Tom: And that coat she made him with spaceships on. That was really naff.

Lucy: Ah, come on! He was only about six.

Paul: True, but last winter, when it was raining, he came to school in a pair of fisherman's waders and he was eleven then.

Jo: He never seems bothered though does he? Even when people laugh.

Caroline: I'd die. If my mum made me do that I'd run away. I'd hide. I'd do anything, but I wouldn't go to school.

Jo: You'd have to. Anyway he's not bothered.

Caroline: He might not be, but I would, and they get you for stuff like that at the High School.

Mike: Yeah they would. They'd laugh at you and take the mickey.

Lucy: That's the bit I don't fancy, all the older ones laughing at you.

Jake: They won't laugh. Our kid says they never bother with you. It's only if you're a real geek or something.

Paul: They do pick on some kids, our Clare says so anyway.

Tom: That's your Clare. People just make up stories.

Caroline: Well what about tying you up in the cloakroom or sticking your head in the toilet?

Tom: They always say that but no-one's ever met anyone it's happened to.

Caroline: My mum said that.

Mike: No she didn't, Tom did. I saw his lips move.

Caroline: You know what I mean.

Paul: Don't go in if they're smoking though.

Jake: Where?

Paul: In the toilets. They get you then.

Jo: I wouldn't go in anyway, I hate smoking.

Caroline: What about the teachers?

Mike: They probably hate it as well.

Caroline: Shut up stupid. They give you loads of homework.

Mike: They don't.

Caroline: They do, and if you don't do it you get detention.

Jake: So do it.

Caroline: And if you get lost between lessons you get detention for being late.

Jo: I'd heard that.

Jake: So don't get lost.

Paul: Yeah, but it's massive. It's not like our school. You have a different room for every lesson.

Lucy: They make you have showers for PE. You have to take all your clothes off and the teachers look at you.

Mike: So what, they're women teachers.

Caroline: That's another thing.

Tom: What?

Caroline: Men teachers. Do you know, ever since we went to school we've never had a man teacher?

Mike: We have.

Caroline: *You* have. You've had Mr Barnes for football and that student for rugby, but we haven't. None of the girls has. All we've ever had is women.

Jake: What's up? Are you afraid or something?

Caroline: *(Indignant)* No!

Jake: Well shut up then!

Caroline: I was just saying, that's all.

Jake: Well it's boring. We've got three weeks holiday left yet. Come on.

Paul: Where to?

Jake: Anywhere.

Jo: Let's go by the Late Shop.

Paul: Why?

Jo: I've got some money. We could get some sweets.

There is general agreement and all exit discussing sweets, how much money Jo has or shouting down Caroline who is still trying to justify herself.

Scene 4 — Assembly Hall

It is the opening assembly of the new school year.

The scene takes place on an open stage in a pool of light, giving the suggestion that we are seeing a small part of a much larger gathering. On the edges of the light can be seen the teachers who feature in subsequent scenes. In particular we see Mr Hartson, Mrs Ratcliffe, Caroline's form tutor and Miss Butterlee the Head of Year.

Miss Butterlee is dressed in a traditional two piece suit with a high necked blouse underneath the jacket. She carries a black leather personal organiser – which she constantly refers to – and wears her spectacles on a gold cord around her neck. Her hair is styled very conventionally. Although she is softly spoken, there is no warmth about Miss Butterlee. She gives out instructions with no hint of humour and is seemingly obsessed with minute details rather than the more general concerns which pupils might have.

Caroline, Jo, Lucy, Tom, Jake, Mike, Paul and others enter.

Miss Butterlee: Come in, sit down quickly, and no talking.

Jo: *(To Caroline)* She seems horrible.

Caroline: Shut up! We'll get done.

Jo: Listen to her.

Miss Butterlee: Hurry up now, come on you two.

Caroline: There's loads here.

Jo: About 200.

Miss Butterlee: Move right along to the end of the row.

Caroline: Are they all Year Seven?

Jo: Course they are, it's the same as on our visit.

Miss Butterlee: That boy. You, yes you, the one with the red hair. Take your coat off. You don't need it on inside school.

Caroline: There just seems like more today. This place is massive and the teachers ...

Jo: *(Seeing Mr Hartson approach)* Look out.

Mr Hartson: You! You there!

Caroline: Me?

Mr Hartson: Yes, you! Who do you think I'm pointing to? And say 'Sir' when you speak to me.

Caroline: Sorry, Sir.

Mr Hartson: Stand up. *(Caroline stands, all eyes are on her)* What's your name?

Caroline: Caroline, Sir.

Mr Hartson: Caroline what? What's your full name?

Caroline: Dearman Sir, Caroline Dearman.

Mr Hartson: Well, Miss Dearman, are you deaf?

Caroline: Pardon Sir?

Mr Hartson: I said, are you deaf? And don't get clever with me.

Caroline: I'm not, Sir.

Mr Hartson: No, you're not, you're not very clever at all if you can't understand simple instructions. Did you hear what Miss Butterlee said?

Caroline: When Sir?

Mr Hartson: Just now. She said no talking, didn't she?

Caroline: Yes Sir.

Mr Hartson: So why are you doing it?

Caroline: I don't know Sir.

Mr Hartson: Of course you don't know, and if you don't learn to listen, you never will. Stand there, please.

Caroline stands there. Mr Hartson returns to his place. Miss Butterlee crosses to the front of the assembly.

Miss Butterlee: Well good morning Year Seven, because that's what you are now, and welcome to Grangemount High School. I hope, to start with, that you've all learned a lesson from this young lady's silliness. *(Indicates Caroline)* The lesson is simple, we have certain rules and standards here at Grangemount and we expect them to be observed, particularly when a pupil has been given a direct instruction. *(To Caroline)* Is that clear young lady?

Caroline: Yes, Miss.

Miss Butterlee: Good, well sit down now and let's have no repetition.

Caroline sits and Miss Butterlee addresses the whole year group again.

Now then, Year Seven, over the next few weeks I'm sure that I will get to know you all and that you will get used to the way we do things here. In a short while you will go with your form teachers to arrange timetables etc. I will visit each form in turn to hand out copies of our code of conduct and to see that you are getting settled, but first, our Headteacher, Mr Marsh, wants a word with you. When Mr Marsh comes in you will all stand and wait for him to tell you to be seated. *(Looking directly at Caroline)* Naturally, there will be no talking.

Mr Marsh enters. The children, as instructed, all rise. He carries with him a folder which contains his notes. He stands behind a lectern and, after pausing to cast an eye over the children, he begins to speak.

Mr Marsh: Please be seated.

The children sit.

Welcome, all of you, to Grangemount High School. Naturally everything will seem a little strange to you, but after your visits with the primary teachers, I'm sure you know your way around already. You've already met Miss Butterlee, your Head of Year, and shortly you will go back with your form tutors to collect your timetables and maps of the school. Naturally we want you to be happy here and free of problems.

Should you have any worries, however minor, then Miss Butterlee and your form teacher are very approachable and they are the people to speak to. They will, I am sure, put your mind at rest. You may not realise it now, but your time at Grangemount is relatively short and, as well as enjoying yourselves, there is work to be done and targets to be achieved.

It is not by coincidence that Grangemount enjoys a good reputation in the area and such reputations have to be earned by all of us in the school community.

Today you are joining that community as junior members. It is up to you to learn the values, obey the rules and strive to do your very best to achieve the highest grades possible.

Good luck and work hard. I am sure that, as time goes on, I will meet many of you on a personal basis. Carry on, Miss Butterlee.

He exits, leaving the children stunned at the shortness of his speech.

Miss Butterlee: Thank you, Mr Marsh. Now Year Seven, please make your way, in silence, for those who need reminding, back to your form rooms where your teacher will direct the next stage of the enrolment process.

As the children leave, a hushed whisper spreads through the pupils and Miss Butterlee's voice rings out.

Miss Butterlee: SILENCE!

The lights go out abruptly.

Scene 5 — The Form Room

The lights come up to reveal the pupils repositioned after assembly. They are now in their form room with Mrs Ratcliffe. They have apparently been there for some time since all the pupils are writing in little booklets and one is at the desk having a sheet of paper checked. Caroline, Jo and Jake are in this form.

Mrs Ratcliffe: Thank you Laura.

The girl returns to her seat.

Right everybody, stop writing, I want a quick word.

The pupils stop writing and look up.

First of all, have I checked everybody's timetable?

The children nod in confirmation.

Good, well that just leaves the personal information sheets to be finished. The most important part is Section 4.

She holds up a sheet of paper and the children examine their copies.

In this section we will be filling in your interests and your ambitions, so I want you to think about that over break. More than anything, we want you to do well at Grangemount and I want to be proud of you as my form. So it's important that I get to know you properly.

A boy at the back of the class raises his hand.

Yes. *(She consults a plan of the class)* John isn't it?

John: Miss, is it true that we have exams after the first week?

Mrs Ratcliffe: No John, it's not. You have assessment tests after half a term so that we know how you've settled and what sets to put you in. There's nothing to worry about.

Another child raises her hand. As the children raise their hands, Mrs Ratcliffe checks her list and brings different pupils into the discussion.

Yes Karen?

Karen: Miss, it isn't really fair though is it? I mean if you're dead clever then tests are always easy.

Mrs Ratcliffe: Well I wouldn't say easy Karen. *(Turning to another child)* Yes Caroline?

Caroline: Sometimes Miss, even if you like a subject, tests are still hard.

There is some sceptical muttering.

Mrs Ratcliffe: Quiet please! There's two sides to the argument. People always find tests hard. If you're not very good at something then it's difficult, but it can be just as difficult when people expect you to do well all of the time. The whole point of these tests is to find the level that suits you in each of the different subjects, and they're not for weeks yet, so don't worry!

The bell rings.

There now, that's the signal for break so collect up your belongings and make your way outside. Don't forget your maps. We don't want anyone getting lost. If there's time, we'll do a quick school tour later this morning. I'll see you all back here in fifteen minutes.

All the children leave. The lights fade.

Scene 6 – Mr Wardle's Shop

The shop is a newsagents, selling sweets, drinks, stationery etc. Mr Wardle has just finished serving a customer when a group of youths clad in fashionable street clothes enter the shop. The apparent leader is Tony, with him are a girl and two other boys. They look round.

Mr Wardle: Can I help you?

Piggy: *(Stepping right up to the counter and indicating Tony)* It's him that wants something.

Mr Wardle: *(To Tony)* What's it to be then?

Tony: *(Standing next to Piggy to obscure Wardle's view)* A packet of them little paper fasteners.

Mr Wardle: You mean paper clips.

19

Tony: No, them brass coloured ones that you thread through and then bend the legs back.

During this conversation Shelley and Bazzer have moved closer to the sweet counter – Mr Wardle is trying to keep an eye on them.

Mr Wardle: We've not had any of them for years.

Piggy: You have, we got some last month.

Mr Wardle: Not from here you didn't.

Tony: We did. The lady who works here found some under the counter.

Mr Wardle: *(Concerned with Shelley and Bazzer)* Well I'll have a quick look for you but I don't think ...

He bends under the counter and, as he does, Shelley and Bazzer start to take sweets. In the same instant, a customer comes in.

Customer: Hey! You two!

Mr Wardle: *(Looking up quickly)* Here, what are you doing?

The four young people dash out of the shop with their theft, knocking the customer aside.

Mr Wardle: *(Moving from behind the counter)* Come back here you little buggers!

Customer: You'll not see them again, or your property.

Mr Wardle: Little buggers, they should be in school the lot of them, they should be in school.

As Mr Wardle says this, the lights fade to darkness.

Scene 7 — The School Yard

It is break time. There are various groups dotted about, some indulging in quite physical and boisterous horseplay. Grouped together in one area of the stage are Caroline, Jo and their friends whom we met in Scene 1. The scene is established with general discussion of the events around them and the morning so far. Two boys 'fighting' accidentally barge Caroline in the back. She is thrown forward and a little shaken.

Caroline: They shouldn't let them in at first.

Mike: Who?

Caroline: The older ones.

Jo: *(Dusting off and fussing round her)* Are you alright?

Caroline: Yes, I think so.

Jake: Why not?

Caroline: Why not what?

Jake: Why not let the older ones in?

Caroline: To give us a chance to settle, so we can find our way around.

Mike: They were here first.

Paul: It's their school.

Caroline: It's supposed to be ours too. That's what they keep saying – we're part of a community.

Mike: So just get on with it. Be part of the community and stop moaning. They have to come here some time.

Caroline: I just meant it's a bit 'in at the deep end' *(Gets blank looks from most of the others)* ... Oh, never mind.

Lucy: I'm dying for a wee.

Mike: Well, go and have one them.

Lucy: I can't.

Paul: Its easy, just remember to take your knickers off or they'll get wet.

Lucy: Very funny. I mean I can't because its full of older kids having a ciggy. They're all locked in the cubicles.

Jo: That's right and when you go in the others all stare at you.

Lucy: That big redhead was in, you know, Ingrid Atherton. She gave me a right look. She's supposed to be dead hard.

Caroline: That's what I mean. Why can't we have our own toilets or a separate part of the yard?

Jake: My dad says you've just got to get on with it.

Lucy: My dad says everyone at this school is on drugs and delinquent. It doesn't mean he's right though.

Tom: Shut up, here's Big Lowther.

They tighten up their huddle but Lowther barges in.

Big Lowther: Hello you lot, seen our Dek?

All: No/ Not today / Might be over there / He's in Mr Sheridan's form.

He turns to Caroline.

Big Lowther: Hello 'Pancakes', give us a crisp *(He seizes a handful without waiting for an answer)* Ta – tell him I was looking for him, see ya.

He goes, smacking Jake hard on the back as he does so.

Caroline: *(To Jo)* So it's just stories is it?

Jo: What are you on about?

Caroline: Big Lowther, after us on the first day.

Jake: He's not after us. That was just Lowther being Lowther. Anyway if you're worried tell Mrs Ratcliffe.

Caroline: You tell her.

Jake: I might, she's dead fit her.

Jo: Well don't let it worry you Jake, Miss Butterlee's more in your league.

General laughter.

Jo: He's right though, you could tell her.

Mike: Well you couldn't tell ours. We've got Hartson. He's horrible.

Paul: He's already given Darren Shawcross lines.

Caroline: What could I tell her? He's not done anything.

Jo: Well there you are then.

Caroline: It's just that ...

The bell interrupts her.

Jake: We'd better get back.

They all get out their maps.

Tom: *(Pointing)* It's this way.

Lucy: No it's not, it's that way.

Caroline: Oh no, we'll get done.

They are all facing in different directions. The lights go out abruptly.

Scene 8 — By the Shelter in the Park

Tony, Piggy, Shelley and Bazzer are clearly out of breath. Tony is bent double, one hand against the shelter. The others are variously sitting/ leaning against the shelter trying to get their breath back. They have run here after their escapade at Mr Wardle's shop.

Tony: That was close, I thought we'd had it then.

Piggy: You said it would be dead easy.

Tony: And it would have been. How was I supposed to know there'd be a copper going past? Anyway Shelley should have warned us about that customer.

Piggy: Yeah, Tony's right. Daft cow!

Shelley: Oi! Get lost, it's not my fault just cos some meddling git walks in is it?

Bazzer: He couldn't 'alf run though, that copper. I thought he'd got us.

Piggy: He nearly did.

Shelley: See his face though, when we went over the railway line?

Bazzer: Yeah, he didn't want to know did he?

Piggy: It was a bit daft though. What if there'd been a train?

Bazzer: Oh, very sorry, I'll bring a timetable next time.

Shelley: Shut it you two. Look, it's mad Jessie.

An older woman enters. She is wearing a woolly hat and a waterproof jacket and carrying a dog lead but there is no sign of a dog.

Shelley: Hey Jessie, where's your dog?

Piggy: Has it run away?

Jessie ignores them.

Tony: Hey Jessie, what's up? Gone deaf?

Jessie exits pursued by the four of them calling out questions about the 'missing' dog and barking. The lights fade to darkness as they all exit.

Scene 9 — Around the School

Mrs Ratcliffe is showing her form around the school. Caroline, Jo and Jake are there with other pupils. The class is still entering when Mrs Ratcliffe begins speaking. She is holding a clipboard.

Mrs Ratcliffe: Come on at the back, keep up or we'll have more absent friends. Won't we Caroline?

Caroline: Yes Mrs Ratcliffe.

Mrs Ratcliffe: I bet this is where the three of you got lost isn't it?

Caroline: I don't know Miss. It all looks the same to me.

Jake: It is Miss. We came from down there, *(pointing)* out of the yard.

Mrs Ratcliffe: And then went that way, *(points)* past the stairs I suppose?

Jo: Yes Miss, we did. That's where that man shouted at us.

Mrs Ratcliffe: Well you needn't worry about Mr Sheldon. It was just a misunderstanding. Just remember, if you come past the stairs, it's left by the drinks machine. Alright Caroline?

Caroline: Yes Miss.

Mrs Ratcliffe: Good! Now, while we're here. *(Looks through the papers on the clipboard)* Yes, I thought so – quite a few of you have written down that you like music.

General murmurs of assent.

Well, make a note of where we are, because that door, *(points to it)* leads to the music rooms and that's where you are this afternoon. And while we're about it, up those stairs – near Mr Sheldon's room, Jake,

Jake looks sheepish.

is the French Department and you're there after Music and before Science. So, which way to the form room, Caroline?

Caroline: *(Looks around uncertainly, then, looking inspired)* Past the stairs and left at the drinks machine.

Mrs Ratcliffe: Very good – lead on there if you will.

Caroline sets off.

Mrs Ratcliffe: Caroline.

Caroline: Yes, Miss?

Mrs Ratcliffe: The stairs are that way Caroline.

Caroline: *(Looking very embarrassed)* Yes, Miss.

She leads them off with the class making a mixture of comments about Caroline, Mrs Ratcliffe and the school. The lights fade to darkness as they exit.

Scene 10 – Caroline's House

It is the evening of the first day at her new school. The set is as before. Dad is at the table arranging some papers into different piles and putting them into his briefcase. Mum and Caroline are seated in easy chairs. Mum has an exercise book and is testing Caroline.

Mum: Hello?

Caroline: Bonjour.

Mum: Goodbye?

Caroline: Au revoir.

Mum: OK? How are you?

Caroline: Ça va?

Mum: Fine, OK.

Caroline: Ça va.

Mum: That's the same.

Caroline: I know.

Mum: But it can't be, you must have it wrong.

Caroline: Why?

Mum: Because they aren't going to have the same word for different things are they?

Caroline: Why not?

Mum: Because it's not logical.

Caroline: No Mum, it's French, and that's what they say. So just test me will you?

Mum: Well, if you say so, but don't come to me if you've copied it down wrong. You're the one who'll get in trouble.

Caroline: Are you helping me or what?

Dad: *(Without looking up)* Don't be rude to your mother Caroline.

Caroline: I'm not being. It's just ...

Dad: *(Still not looking up)* She only wants you to do well. We both do.

Caroline: Yes Dad ...

There is a silence.

Mum: *(Trying to jolly things up)* Come on, only one left – 'My name is ...?'

Caroline: Je m'appelle.

Mum: Well done, that's all of them.

Dad: *(Looking up for the first time)* That's it? You've only done about half a dozen.

Caroline: Five.

Dad: Even less! Is that supposed to be homework? How are you supposed to learn ...?

Mum: It is only the first day John. Give her a chance.

Dad: I suppose so but ...

Mum: Tell us about Music.

Caroline: It's a collection of notes arranged in a melodic way ...

Dad: Very funny. Never mind Music, what about Science?

Caroline: I've told you, we didn't do anything in Science. They put us in groups and ...

Dad: And which one are you in? I hope it's the top one.

Caroline: Not that sort of group. They just mixed us up, then they gave us exercise books, then we went with Miss Murgatroyd.

Dad: Who?

Caroline: Miss Murgatroyd, she's the teacher. She seems dead nice.

Mum: Very nice.

Caroline: *(Rolling her eyes)* Very nice. And we filled in these data sheets for the computer.

Dad: Why?

Caroline: *(Sarcastic, though Dad doesn't hear)* Cos the computer couldn't do it on its own.

Mum: *(Glancing at Dad)* So, what about Music?

Caroline: That was great. We got split into groups and we had to go with Mr Timothy. He had this awful Winnie the Pooh tie on, but he's dead good on the piano. He says we'll get to do all kinds of instruments and sing. Can I have Grandad's violin out of the loft and learn that?

Dad: It's quite valuable that instrument. It's not a toy.

Caroline: I want to learn it, not play with it. Well I do want to play with it, obviously, but music, not games and anyway, no-one uses it.

Dad: I know that. I'm just making it clear that ...

Mum: Look, why not get the details properly and then we'll see.

Caroline: They'll be giving out letters in the next couple of weeks.

Mum: Well we can sort it out then. Now go and pack your bag ready for tomorrow and I'll make you some supper.

Caroline exits upstairs, Mum to the kitchen. Dad continues with his papers as the lights fade to darkness.

Scene 11 — Outside the Music Room

In the corridor, the form are waiting for a lesson. Caroline has her bag and is carrying a violin. Big Lowther approaches, the group react. Caroline is talking to Jo and doesn't see him. He comes right up behind her pulling faces. She steps back onto his foot. He calls out.

Big Lowther: Aagh! Look out, Pancakes! Look what you're doing.

Caroline: Sorry Lowther, I didn't see you.

Big Lowther: No, Pancakes, that's cos you're thick. You've not been here five minutes and you think you own the place.

Jake:	Half a term.
Big Lowther:	What?
Jake:	We've been here nearly half a term.
Big Lowther:	So what? You're still too cocky. I'm going to have to sort you out Jakey boy.
Jake:	Oh aye, you got a gang then Lowther?
Big Lowther:	*(Clearly bravado)* You'll see Jake. Just watch your back, that's all.

The class just laugh this off. Lowther turns to Caroline.

Big Lowther:	Anyway *(indicates violin)* what's all this then, Pancakes?
Caroline:	It's a violin.
Big Lowther:	*(Laughing)* Bit snotty isn't it *(puts on a posh voice).* the violin?

Caroline says nothing.

	But then you are, aren't you?
Caroline:	What?
Big Lowther:	Snotty. Our Dek says you're dead snotty and stuck up.
Lucy:	What's snotty about a violin then?
Big Lowther:	You just don't, do you?
Lucy:	No, *you* don't, but Caroline does.
Mike:	And she's good at it
Jake:	Anyway, what's wrong with Caroline being clever?
Caroline:	Jake!
Jake:	Well, you are. What's wrong with that?
Lucy:	And your Dek's in all the same classes.
Mike:	So what's that make him?
Big Lowther:	*(Leaving)* Get lost kiddies, all sticking up for each other. See ya, Pancakes.

He exits.

Caroline: He'll be after me now.

Lucy: Why?

Caroline: You lot going on about me being clever.

Jake: Well you are.

Caroline: Not that clever. He'll just call me a swot now.

Jake: So what? Look Caroline you're clever so get on with it. Lowther's not thick you know.

Caroline: Isn't he?

Lucy: No, he won the Geography Award last year.

Mike: And he's in top set English with our Greg.

Caroline: So why's he call me names?

Jake: He probably fancies you.

Mike: No, it's just the fashion.

Caroline: Oh, well thanks, Mike.

Mike: No, I mean he might fancy you, but it's just the fashion. People try to look hard by calling you snotty.

Caroline: Well what about 'Pancakes'? Why does he call me 'Pancakes'?

There is a silence. Everyone looks embarrassed.

Caroline: What's up? Best tell me.

Lucy: It's because you've got no boobs.

Caroline: What?

Lucy: He calls you 'Pancakes' because you've got no boobs. Flat chest. *(Pause)* Get it?

There is a silence. The others struggle to contain their laughter.

Caroline: *(Angry, puts her hand to her chest)* I have *(pause, looks at the others)* I have got boobs. *(Shouts after Lowther)* You dirty pig Lowther. *(To the group)* He's a pervert he is. *(Shouts down corridor)* You're a pervert you are Lowther.

As Caroline shouts, Miss Butterlee appears with Mr Hartson and the rest of the group react. Caroline remains unaware of their presence.

What's up? Don't look like that. I've had enough. I'm sick of this school and I'm sick of him. Never mind my boobs, I bet he's only got a little dick. *(Shouting after Lowther)* I bet you've only got a little dick, Lowther.

Miss Butterlee: Caroline Dearman, what is the meaning of this?

Caroline: *(Shocked)* Miss Butterlee!

Miss Butterlee: That's right and I repeat, what is the meaning of this?

Caroline: Nothing, I just ...

Miss Butterlee: It certainly didn't sound like nothing. *(Turns to the others)* What are you all doing here?

All: Music, Miss / Waiting for Mr Timothy, Miss.

Miss Butterlee: Well wait inside the room.

The group exits. Miss Butterlee looks at Caroline.

I am, frankly, astonished Caroline.

Caroline attempts to speak. Miss Butterlee silences her with a raised hand.

For a Year Seven pupil, a girl indeed, to be shouting such things down a corridor is ... *(pause)* well, I don't know what it is, it's just astonishing.

Mr Hartson: And we had the same sort of outburst in my Maths lesson the other day.

Miss Butterlee: And what was that all about?

Mr Hartson: She threw a book at Derek Lowther, didn't you Caroline?

Caroline: It wasn't like that Miss Butterlee. He was picking on me, he always does.

Mr Hartson: And I told you at the time, ignore it. You're not at school to make friends, you're here to learn. Take my advice and a bright girl like you will do very well.

Caroline: But Sir, he was ...

Miss Butterlee: Whatever he was doing you shouldn't have been throwing books and you shouldn't have been shouting obscenities down the corridor. There is simply no excuse for that kind of behaviour. Is there Caroline?

Caroline: But Miss ...

Miss Butterlee fixes her with a stare.

No, Miss.

She hangs her head.

Miss Butterlee: You do know that the half term review starts tomorrow don't you Caroline?

Caroline: Yes, Miss.

Miss Butterlee: And what sort of impression do you think this makes?

Caroline: I don't know, Miss.

Miss Butterlee: Well I know, Caroline, I know! What if I'd been a visitor to the school, what then?

Caroline is silent.

We look at behaviour as well as test results in the half term review you know.

Caroline: Yes, Miss.

Miss Butterlee: When's your first assessment?

Caroline: Tomorrow Miss, in Maths with Mr Hartson.

Mr Hartson: And I'm hoping for big things. I've told them all, Miss Butterlee, Hartson's standards are high standards.

Miss Butterlee: Do you enjoy Maths, Caroline?

Caroline: No, Miss, I ...

Mr Hartson: Oh, there's no doubting that she can do it, it's just that now and then we get these unfortunate outbursts. It's a pity she's not so outgoing when it comes to answering questions.

Caroline says nothing.

Miss Butterlee: Well, I'm afraid you leave me no alternative, Caroline, I shall have to contact your parents.

Caroline: But Miss! ...

Miss Butterlee: It's no good Caroline. From the first day, talking in assembly, to this outburst in Maths, and as for this shouting in the corridor, well, who knows what you've been up to. We had very high hopes when you came to us Caroline, and we've a responsibility to your parents to see you do your best. Come to me after final lesson. There'll be a letter for your parents.

Caroline: Yes, Miss.

Miss Butterlee: And Caroline ...

Caroline: Yes, Miss?

Miss Butterlee: See that you come. We don't want that adding to your catalogue of failures.

Caroline: No, Miss.

Caroline exits to the Music Room, Miss Butterlee and Mr Hartson along the corridor as the lights fade to darkness.

Scene 12 — Caroline's House

Caroline and her mother are seated. Mr Dearman is on his feet pacing up and down reading extracts from Miss Butterlee's letter.

Dad: Disruptive in assembly, violent behaviour in Mathematics, shouting obscenities down the corridor. Has there been a day when you've behaved yourself since you went to this school?

Caroline: It wasn't like that.

Dad: Well, Miss *(looks at letter)* Butterlee seems to think so.

Caroline: Well it wasn't.

Dad: Well what was it like? *(Pause)* Well?

Caroline: He'd just been rude to me.

Dad: So you thought you'd shout obscenities at him?

Caroline: No.

Dad: Well Miss Butterlee seems to thinks so.

Caroline: I did shout.

Dad: Oh, progress at last. You finally admit it, you did shout obscenities down a corridor. And tell me, *(sarcastic)* now you come to think of it, did you perhaps disrupt an assembly and behave violently in Maths as well, or was Miss Butterlee dreaming that?

Caroline: It wasn't like that.

Dad: So you keep saying, but you don't seem very keen to tell me what it was like.

Caroline: It was an accident, it just sounds bad.

Dad: An accident?

Caroline: Not an accident exactly, it was ...

Dad: Listen, young lady, we'd better get a few things straight here. My daughter, *(looks at Mum)* **our** daughter, doesn't have accidents like this. Do you understand?

Caroline: Yes Dad.

Dad: Just listen to this, *(reads from letter)* 'Caroline's involvement is an added disappointment when combined with the remarks of at least one other teacher who notes an increasing reluctance to take part in lessons and an unwillingness to answer questions.' And what does that mean?

Caroline: That's Mr Hartson that. He said that today.

Dad: Well?

Caroline: Well what?

Mum: Do you answer Mr Hartson's questions Caroline?

Caroline: Not all of them no, no-one does. You get laughed at if you've always got your hand up.

Dad: Oh I see, you won't do your work because some thickie laughs at you?

Caroline: It's not thickies. It's Lucy, Jake, everyone. You don't answer all the questions, it's a game, MEWAB *(Pronounced phonetically as a word.)*

Dad: MEWAB, what are you talking about?

Caroline: That's what people say when you answer a question, it means, 'Make 'em work a bit'.

Mum: Let me get this straight. You have a game not to answer questions?

Caroline: Not in every lesson.

Mum: In some lessons?

Caroline: Yes.

Mum: And this MEWAB – make 'em work a bit – it's to make life difficult for the teachers?

Caroline: Not exactly.

Mum: Well what then?

Caroline: Well, if you answer all the questions, it's creeping. So we, sort of take it in turns and say MEWAB. It's meant to be a laugh.

Dad: Well no-one here thinks it's funny. You're supposed to be at school to work. Do you realise that?

Caroline: Yes.

Dad: You've tests coming up, haven't you?

Caroline: Yes Dad.

Dad: They start tomorrow.

Caroline: I know.

Dad: Well, what do you think of this then? *(Reads from the letter)* 'Caroline's difficulty in settling may well affect her half termly review. Whilst the school recognises that she is an able pupil academically, her general attitude paints a different picture ... blah, blah, blah ... performance in these tests combined with a pupil's behaviour record serve as deciding factors when subject sets are created and reports compiled etc., etc.' Need I say more?

Caroline: No Dad.

Dad: Well get this straight. Things are going to change around here. These tests are important and if you don't do well, there'll be trouble. If you won't work, you'll be made to work.

Caroline: But Dad ...

Dad: Never mind 'but Dad'. I've told you time and time again, day after day, what's expected of you, and this *(waves the letter)* is what we get. Well it's not good enough and you can get to your room and start doing something about it. Go on, get up there.

Caroline rushes from the room, Mum and Dad look at her as she exits. They remain in this position as the lights fade to darkness.

Scene 13 — Outside School

It is the start of the school day. Jo is waiting outside the school for Caroline who is apparently late. Whilst she is waiting, various other pupils go past, engaged in their own conversations. Some say hello to Jo, who is constantly checking her watch. Paul and Mike enter.

Paul: Hiya, Jo. You coming in?

Jo: No, I'm waiting for Caroline.

Mike: You'll be late.

Jo: No, there's time yet. I'll see you inside.

They go.

Mike & Paul: See you.

There is a brief pause during which other pupils pass. Jo checks her watch, looks around and fidgets anxiously. Lucy enters.

Lucy: Hiya, Jo. What you doing?

Jo: I'm waiting for Caroline, but she's dead late.

Lucy: You'll get done. You want to leave her.

Jo: No, there's ten minutes yet. She'll be here.

Lucy exits. Almost simultaneously Caroline arrives. She is carrying her violin case.

Jo: Where've you been? It's nearly ten to.

Caroline: I got up late and then I forgot my violin, my mum called me back so that meant I missed the first bus.

Jo: You're always doing that recently, getting up late, forgetting your violin.

Caroline: Losing it would be better still.

Jo: *(Surprised)* What? A couple of weeks ago you thought it was great.

Caroline: A couple of weeks ago, people weren't making fun of me all the time.

Jo: They're only joking.

Caroline: It's alright for you, it's me they make fun of.

Jo: About three people, maximum. It's mostly Lowther.

Caroline: Yeah well I'm giving it up and that's it.

Jo: But you're dead good, Mr Timothy said ...

Caroline: You're starting to sound like my mother.

Jo: Sorry. *(Pause)* We'll have to hurry up you know. We've got that Maths test first lesson.

Caroline: Don't remind me. My dad's been on about it for the last week.

Jo: You're stupid you. I don't know why you tell them in the first place.

Caroline: It just slipped out and he's not shut up since. Anyway Butterlee put it in that letter. I know I'm going to do badly, but I daren't tell him.

Jo: Badly? I wish I was going to do that badly.

Caroline: You'll do alright.

Jo: And so will you, so stop going on.

Caroline: Yes, but alright isn't good enough for my dad. Everything's got to be brilliant. I just can't keep it up. I hate it, I really hate it at this school.

Jo: You don't. It's just ...

Caroline: I do, right from the first day, getting lost in the corridors, yobs like Lowther, teachers you don't know shouting at you. Do you know, that one with the beard and specs called me a thicko yesterday?

Jo: He didn't mean it.

Caroline: How do you know? They don't care who they're shouting at, and that letter ... my dad went ballistic. Nothing's ever good enough. It's as if ...

Jo: Caroline, don't you think you're just a teeny bit over the top?

Caroline: Look, if anyone asks, you haven't seen me.

Jo: What?

Caroline: I'm off. I'm not going in to school.

Jo: Don't be stupid, where will you go?

Caroline: I don't know. The shops, anywhere.

Jo: You'll get done.

Caroline: You haven't seen me. *(She runs off.)*

Jo: *(Shouting after her)* Caroline!

Jo leaves, reluctantly, in the direction of school

ACT 2

Scene 1 — By the Park Shelter

The scene is once again the local park. Caroline is wandering along aimlessly. For a period of time she remains alone and it is clear from her actions, kicking stones, examining the stitching on her shoes, trying to walk a straight line etc. that she has no real idea of what she wants to do or how she will fill her day. After her first lines she moves upstage and sits on the bench inside the shelter. Through her first lines, we discover that the shelter faces a bowling green.

She puts her bag and violin case on the ground and steps onto the bowling green. She carries out the pantomime gestures of a bowls game and talks to herself as if she was a commentator.

Caroline: ... and so with only one wood to play in a game only slightly less exciting than sleeping sickness, the almost senile Mrs Jocelyn Spam-Fritter steps up to see what is required, and, as she does so, it is worth remembering that only recently she lost her husband in that tragic incident with the food processor, making the chance of victory here all the more remarkable. And, at the second the wood leaves her hand, there is joy on her face. She knows and her partner knows, and the crowd knows, and the viewing public knows

At this point, Caroline stops her 'game' and, during the monologue about noses, picks up her bag and violin and goes to the shelter finally flopping down onto the seat with the word 'crap'.

and the big nose and the little nose and the Roman nose and the broken nose and the scabby, rotten, horrible, runny, green, snotty nose and the ... crap!

There is a brief pause before she takes sandwiches from her bag and begins to eat one.

Tony emerges from behind the bench where he has been concealed for some time. He is about 15 years of age and dressed in fashionable street clothes. His sudden appearance shocks Caroline and she squeezes up to the end of the bench.

Tony: Give us a bite then.

No reply. Caroline just stares.

> Come on, give us a bit of your butty. *(Pause)* Look,
> it's my shed and you're in it, so that's the rent.
> *(Pause)* I wont hurt you, you know. I only want a bit.
> Keep it, if you're that bothered. It's probably got
> cucumber on anyway. *(He folds his arms and says
> nothing)*

*Caroline gingerly holds out a sandwich to him. He takes it and looks
inside.*

> I was right, cucumber *(he discards the cucumber)*
> and tuna on wholemeal bread. Very nice. (*He eats*)

Caroline: My mum gives them to me. She says they're good
for me.

Tony: She's probably right. They're definitely good for me.
Got any more?

She gives him the packet and he continues to eat.

> Who won then?

Caroline: What?

Tony: Who won the bowls?

Caroline: Oh I don't know, it was tragic. Mrs Spam-Fritter's
partner collapsed with all the excitement.

Tony: Good job it wasn't golf then.

Caroline: Why?

Tony: Cos in golf, they'd have counted it as a stroke.

He is pleased with his joke and laughs. Caroline is unmoved.

> It's a joke. Strokes, that's how they score in golf.

Caroline: I get it. I just didn't think it was very funny. *(Pause)*
What did you mean, this is your shed?

Tony: I come here every day, not just me, there's a few of
us. We always meet here. You can get in through the
boards at the back and stash your gear underneath.
That's where I was when you were playing bowls.

Caroline: You come here every day? Shouldn't you be at school?

Tony: Shouldn't *you*?

Caroline: Yes but ...

Tony: There you are then. This your first time?

Caroline: What?

Tony: Wagging it.

Caroline: Oh right. *(Pause)* Yeah, I just ran off this morning. I've been down by the canal most of the day. I'm going to get really done.

Tony: Only if they find out. Acting normal, that's what counts. The first thing to do is to head for home. That's what all the others do. Then they suspect nothing. It's nearly 4 o'clock now so you'll have to get back soon.

Caroline: Then what?

Tony: Then you leave home as normal tomorrow and you just come here. You can meet all the others. Bring some stuff to change into. You can hide your bag under the seat. We'll phone the school, tell them you're ill.

Caroline: Are you mad? We'll never get away with that.

Tony: Course we will, I'm an expert. Just come tomorrow, you'll see.

Caroline looks doubtful.

You'd better go now. You don't want to get into trouble. I'll see you tomorrow.

Caroline: What about you? Aren't you going home?

Tony: I don't need to. My lot know I never go to school. I'll see you tomorrow, by the gate. Now you'd better get off. See you.

Caroline: See you.

She begins her exit as the lights fade to black out.

41

Scene 2 – Outside Caroline's House

Jo knocks at the door. Caroline opens it.

Jo: *(Annoyed)* Where've you been?

Caroline: Oh, it's you.

Jo: Yes, it's me. Where've you been?

Caroline: Around.

Jo: I had to lie for you. Ratcliffe, Jake, everyone – they were all asking for you.

Caroline: I went to the park.

Jo: Oh lovely – take a picnic? You were supposed to be at school.

Caroline: I know that, I just didn't fancy it – it's easier this way.

Jo: *(Sarcastic)* Oh, I can see that, much easier, just don't turn up. I mean no-one's going to notice, or ask where you've been.

Caroline: I'm going to phone the school office.

Jo: *(Shouting)* What? Have you gone mad?

Caroline: Keep your voice down. Who's going to know? No-one will check.

Jo: And then what? You have to come back sometime.

Caroline: Then I'll write a note. You could sign it for me.

Jo: Oh no, no chance. I'll keep my mouth shut over this but I'm not forging notes.

Caroline: You better had keep your mouth shut.

Jo: You're not fair you know, Caroline. You're dropping me in it as well. The teachers will ask me. I'll have to lie.

Caroline: I'll be back in a day or two. It will be fine, honest. Just till the tests are over.

Jo: And then what? *(Pause)* What about the report and everything?

Caroline: I'll think of something. It'll be alright, honest.

Jo: It won't be, it can't be.

Mum: *(From inside)* Who is it, Caroline?

Caroline: It's Jo.

Mum: *(From inside)* Well, bring her in, it's freezing with that door open.

Caroline: OK! *(To Jo)* Just keep your mouth shut, OK?

Jo: Oh don't worry about me, I'm going.

She exits. Caroline watches her leave as the lights fade to darkness.

Scene 3 – The Telephone Box

Tony is in a telephone box. Caroline, wearing school uniform, is waiting outside. Tony, it appears, is on the telephone to school.

Tony: Yes that's right, Caroline Dearman, she's in 7R. *(Pause)* Well I'm not very sure. She's been up all night and I'm taking her to the doctor's later on. *(Pause)* Yes, I'll get in touch tomorrow and let you know. That's OK. Goodbye.

He hangs up.

Caroline: Is that it? Did they believe you?

Tony: Course they did. Why wouldn't they?

Caroline: Dunno, it's just that ...

Tony: We always do it this way. Don't worry, they don't know what your dad sounds like. C'mon, you can get changed at the shed.

They exit. The lights fade to darkness

Scene 4 – The Park Shelter

Tony is standing with his back to the shelter. Caroline is finishing changing behind him.

Tony: Are you ready yet?

Caroline: Nearly.

Tony: Once you start, it's dead easy. By the time they realise, there's nothing they can do.

Caroline: Don't they take you to court?

Tony: In the end, but it takes them ages. Anyway, if you go back for a bit after the final letter, it cocks them up. They haven't got enough people to follow it up. My mum got done once, so I went back for a while.

Caroline: Did you hate it?

Tony: Just not very good at it. I suppose it's not too bad, for a while. Mostly you can get away without doing much. I learned that in the infants. Sharpen your pencil a lot, queue up at the desk, go to the toilet, there's all sorts you can do and they're too busy to stop you.

Caroline: They must catch you sometimes, they're not stupid.

Caroline has got changed and stored her bag under the bench during this dialogue.

Tony: I didn't say they were. Just busy. Here come the others.

Caroline: *(Straightening her clothes)* What others?

Tony: The others that hang out here, Shelley, Piggy, Bazzer, that lot.

Caroline: What if they don't like me?

Tony: It's not up to them. It's not their park, they don't own the shelter. Just keep quiet at first. They're here now.

Bazzer and Shelley arrive followed closely by Piggy and Ingrid.

Tony: Hiya.

All: Hiya / Okay? / Alright?

Caroline tries to look unobtrusive. The others begin taking off ties, changing coats, putting on sweatshirts etc. and hiding bags at the back of the bench.

Shelley: *(Indicating Caroline)* Who's she?

Tony: This is Caroline, she's hanging out here.

Piggy: Why? This is our place. Why can't she go somewhere else?

Tony: It's a public park, Piggy. How can it be ours?

Bazzer: Well it's our shelter. We made the hiding place.

Shelley: So why's she come sticking her nose in? Who's she going to tell?

Tony: She won't tell anyone. I asked her to come. She wagged school yesterday and I told her to come back. You'd have known if you'd been here.

Shelley: Look, I'm just saying, nobody bothers us here. You can keep dry, do what you want. If she grasses us up, then we'll have to get somewhere else.

Ingrid: And if you kick her out, she'll definitely grass us up. *(To Caroline)* What's your name?

Caroline: Caroline. Caroline Dearman.

Ingrid: And what school do you go to Caroline Dearman?

Caroline: Grangemount, I started in September.

Ingrid: *(Laughing)* It's only the middle of October now. Didn't you like it then?

Caroline: There was all these tests. My dad was going on at me and then Mr Hartson, the Maths teacher ...

Ingrid: Oh he's a dog him. I have him. *(Pause)* Don't look so surprised, I go there.

Caroline: *(Getting a bit of confidence)* I'm **not** surprised. You're Ingrid Atherton aren't you?

Ingrid: How do you know that?

Caroline: Everyone knows you. You go smoking in Main Block toilets and none of us can get in. Everyone says you're dead hard.

Ingrid: *(Feeling quite proud of herself)* Yeah, well I suppose I am. So there's your reason for not grassing on us.

Caroline: I wasn't going to anyway. I don't know why I came today, I just ...

Piggy: *(Leaping off the bench)* Ay up everyone! Here's Jessie.

The gang jump to their feet as Jessie enters. She is dressed as before in jacket and woollen hat and is, once again, carrying a dog lead.

Tony: Hey Jessie!

As Jessie turns, the gang begin to shout after her. They call out a variety of dog like calls – 'here boy', 'good dog' etc. They also whistle, and bark. They all think it's tremendously funny. Caroline has no idea what is going on and stands speechless.

Jessie: Have you lot got nothing better to do?

The jeering continues.

You think you're so clever don't you?

Piggy: Do you know you've lost your dog?

The gang falls about laughing.

Bazzer: You should phone the police. They might have a lead.

Shelley: She's got one of them.

Jessie: *(She stands and looks at them shaking her head. Their behaviour is clearly beyond her)* Bunch of wasters, the lot of you. You're not clever you know.

Piggy: Clever enough to know where my dog is.

Jessie: You know what's sad? *(Pause)* Your lives must be very boring if I'm so interesting.

Shelley: Who said you were interesting?

Jessie: Well, you give me plenty of attention. *(Pause)*

Perhaps it'll stop now. *(Indicates Caroline)* Now you've got a new pet of your own.

She exits shaking her head while the gang shout after her.

Caroline: Who was that?

Tony: Mad Jessie.

Caroline: Why do you call her that?

Bazzer: She comes through here every morning, and then later on after lunch, carrying a dog lead.

Piggy: But we've never seen a dog. She just carries the lead.

Caroline: Why?

Piggy: Why what?

Caroline: Why does she carry a dog lead?

There is a pause. No-one has thought of this question before.

Tony: Dunno, never asked her.

Caroline: Why not? Don't you want to know?

Shelley: What for? Why should we?

Caroline: She must have a reason. And why did she say I was your pet?

The others look puzzled. They have no answer.

Shelley: Cos maybe that's what you are, following Tony round like a little puppy.

Caroline: I'm just ...

Tony: I asked her to come.

Shelley: *(To Tony)* Well we didn't. *(Turns to Caroline)* So go back to school and mind your own business. Right?

She continues to stare at Caroline as the lights abruptly cut to blackout.

Scene 5 — The Park Playground

A number of Caroline's friends are there. Caroline is sitting separately from the others. Everyone seems a little subdued. Jo approaches Caroline.

Jo: Look, they came because they like you.

Caroline: When you phoned, you said it would just be us. 'Meet up in the park for a chat.' Huh!

She tosses her head and turns away.

Jo: Well you can talk to them as well. What difference does it make?

The others begin to approach.

Caroline: The difference is that now everyone knows that I'm wagging it and I didn't want that.

Jo: Well, perhaps you should have...

She stops short.

Caroline: Yes? Perhaps what?

Jo: Nothing.

Caroline: It was *some*thing. *(She's getting annoyed)* Perhaps I should have what?

Jo: I just meant that ...

Jake: *(Jake helps her out)* Perhaps you should have told us anyway. We are your mates.

Caroline: Well I couldn't tell you. I mean I didn't plan it. I just got fed up and nicked off.

Lucy: Well, tell *them* that. Tell your mum and dad, before it gets any worse.

Caroline: I can't, not just yet, not till these tests are over.

Mike: Forget the tests, they're not even important.

Caroline: Tell my dad that. He'd love you.

Paul: He'd understand if you explained.

Caroline: Oh yes. Hey, Dad, by the way I've lied about school,

I've been wagging it and I got this lad who I just met to phone up and pretend he was you.

Lucy: Is that what you did?

Caroline: Yes.

Lucy: You're mad.

Tom: So what are you going to do now?

Caroline: I'll just hang on till after the tests, then I'll go back. That's why I don't want everyone knowing.

All: Well we won't tell / No problem / OK etc.

Caroline: Well, I wanted a bit of help actually.

All: *(At the same time)* Sure / Yes / Fine / No problem etc.

Caroline: Well, I'm going to need some info to copy into my homework diary and I'll need a look at one of the assessment reviews.

Jo: How you going to get one of those? Your mum and dad will be expecting it.

Caroline: That's what I mean. I'll get a look at one of yours, then I'll print one up on my computer. It doesn't have to be perfect, I mean they've never seen one before. So as long as it looks convincing.

Jake: You'll never get away with that.

Tom: Lucy's right! You *are* mad. If you're going to do all this, why not just come back?

Lucy: Come back Caroline. They're picking the netball team soon. You'd easily get in.

Jo: And we're joining the choir.

Paul: Miss Markham and Mr Greaves are doing a French trip at Easter. We're all going. You could come on that.

Mike: Just tell them the truth. It's got to be better than this.

Caroline: *(Angry and defensive)* Oh yeah? What do you know?

We have a great time. There's a whole crowd of us. Ingrid Atherton comes and her mate Shelley, she's dead nice.

Jo: Caroline, just ...

Caroline: And Tony. He's got a car so we go off in that. And this woman Jessie she brings her dog down. We were playing with him today. It's better than school any day.

Jake: You'll have to come back some time.

Paul: We just want to help.

Caroline: Well show me that stuff I want and keep your mouths shut.

She looks at each of them. They stare at the ground and are clearly despairing.

Caroline: I've got to go and you've all got to do your homework. *(She laughs)* Don't worry so much. See you. Have a good time at school.

She runs off, they stare after her. The lights fade to blackout.

Scene 6 – The Park Shelter

It is quite early in the morning. Caroline is emerging from beneath the seat of the shelter. She has just got changed. As she hides her bag, Jessie, carrying her dog lead, passes and speaks.

Jessie: Hello then. Spending a lot of time with these wasters aren't you?

Caroline: *(Surprised)* Oh, hello. It's you.

Jessie: That's right. This is me and that, over there, where you're standing, that's you.

Caroline: No, ... I'm sorry ... I meant ... I was just surprised that's all.

Jessie: I suppose I did sort of creep up on you.

Caroline: *(Very uneasy glancing from side to side)* Yes, you made me jump.

Jessie: Are you alright, only ... *(She realises why Caroline is uneasy)* Oh, I see, I'm a stranger and you're on your own. Making you uncomfortable is it?

Caroline: Well, sorry, but it's just ...

Jessie: *(Holding up her hands and backing away)* No, no, don't be sorry. It's not your fault. You're quite right. It's a sad old world, but you're quite right. You don't know me, only ever seen me once.

Caroline: I don't really think you're weird or anything, it's just ... well ... you just get told to be careful, that's all.

Jessie: You're right. No need to explain. *(Pause)* Course, if you were in school, like you should be, then there'd be nothing to worry about anyway.

Caroline: No.

Jessie: That's what made me speak really.

Caroline: What?

Jessie: You. *(Pause)* I don't normally bother talking to the others, get no sense if I did, but you, you seem different.

Caroline: Why?

Jessie: Don't know really, just your looks, you're younger and you weren't shouting when they all did.

Caroline: No. *(Pause)* Do they always do that? Shout, I mean.

Jessie: When they're here, when they see me, aye.

Caroline: You, you don't seem *(pause)* mad.

Jessie: Is that what they say? Is that what they told you? I'm mad?

Caroline: Yeah, they call you Mad Jessie.

Jessie: *(Snorts derisively to herself)* Hmph.

Caroline: It's because of the dog lead.

Jessie looks at it

Why do you always have it?

Jessie: There now, you see, you are different. Them others, all the times they've seen me, all the shouting they've done and not once have they asked why I have a dog lead. But you, first chance you get, you ask.

Caroline: So why do you? Why do you have a lead?

Jessie: Because I've got a dog. That simple. I keep him in kennels up Thorndike Road.

Caroline: Next to Stonehouse Farm?

Jessie: That's right.

Caroline: But why? Why have a dog and keep him there?

Jessie: Cos he's a greyhound. He's called Jessie's Joy, cos that's what he is and if I keep him there I've fields to walk him in and the staff I need to train him. I've not even got a garden at my house.

Caroline: But isn't it a bit strange? A woman with a greyhound?

Jessie: You mean, am I perhaps a bit mad after all?

Caroline: No I don't mean that. You just don't expect it, that's all.

Jessie: Which is one of the main reasons I did it, because people didn't expect me to.

Caroline: But why?

Jessie: Because all my life I've done what other people wanted – my parents, my kids, my husband, especially my husband. So when he died, I decided to do what I wanted for a change, instead of cooking and cleaning and doing as I was told.

Caroline: But why a greyhound?

Jessie: Because I've always liked animals and a greyhound seemed that bit different. Mind you, once I started, I realised it wasn't that different. There are any number of women who own or train dogs.

Caroline: Didn't that put you off?

Jessie: Quite the reverse. It made me more determined.

Showed me what I'd been missing.

Caroline: So how long have you had him?

Jessie: Since he was three months. I bought him in Ireland.

Caroline: It must cost a lot.

Jessie: A bit, aye, but it's my hobby, it's what I spend my money on. Better that than cigarettes and wild living.

Caroline: I suppose so. *(Pause)* And is he good, this dog? Has he won loads of races?

Jessie: Hasn't even run yet, too young. He's only fifteen months. He's got a puppy race coming up. I'm getting him ready.

Caroline: But why? Twelve months for nothing.

Jessie: Oh, it's not for nothing. I've told you he's Jessie's Joy. He's mine, he's my freedom and I love him.

Caroline: But how do you know he's any good?

Jessie: I don't, not for certain. But the lads down there reckon he's a good 'un and anyway, that's not the point. Just watching him, that's enough. He's sleek, he's powerful and when he's yours, it's just brilliant.

Caroline: But what if he loses?

Jessie: Won't know till we try, will we? As the saying goes 'If you aren't in, you can't win.' And that's not the point, I told you, it's my hobby, the decisions are all mine. It's something I've always wanted, and I love him, he's a belting dog.

Caroline: But when will you know for certain?

Jessie: Only a week or so. He runs over at St. Helens.

There's a shout offstage: 'Jessie!'.

Ah well, I'd better be off. It's your so called mates.

Caroline: They're alright really. *(Pause, she feels she has to explain)* They aren't really me mates it's just ...

Jessie: Well remember that. *(Pause)* What's your name?

Caroline: Caroline. Caroline Dearman.

Jessie: Well remember that as well, and take it from me, they aren't your mates. They'll drop you in it. School's where you should be.

Caroline: Maybe.

Jessie: Definitely, so think on. See you Caroline.

Caroline: See you Jessie. And say hello to Jessie's Joy for me.

Jessie: Aye.

She exits as Piggy, Bazzer and Shelley come rushing on stage. They shout after her.

All: Hey Jessie where's your dog? / Has Rover done a runner? / Woof-Woof etc.

Bazzer: What did she want?

Caroline: Nothing much. We were just talking.

Piggy: You want to watch who you're talking to, there's some right weirdos about.

Caroline: Yeah, thanks.

Shelley: What you here for anyway?

Caroline: *(Embarrassed)* I don't know, *(pause)* I just ... *(pause)* Tony said ...

Shelley: *(Mimicking)* Tony said. *(She turns and shouts offstage)* Hey Tony, it's your little mate.

Tony: *(Tony appears)* What?

Shelley: Your pet schoolkid's here.

Tony: Who? *(Sees Caroline)* Oh right, yeah. Hiya Caroline.

Caroline: *(Glad of a friendly face)* Hiya Tony!

Shelley: *(Mimicking)* Hiya Tony.

Tony: Leave off Shelley.

Shelley: Get rid of her.

Piggy: She's alright. What's wrong with her?

Shelley: She's just a kid, we don't want her. I told her that last week.

Tony: Leave her be, she's doing no harm. *(To Caroline)* You're one of us, aren't you Caroline?

Caroline: Yeah, course I am.

Tony: That's OK then. Say hello to everyone.

Caroline: Right yeah. Hiya everyone.

The others grunt and acknowledge her half-heartedly. There is a silence which Caroline fills with a question.

Caroline: Where's Ingrid?

Shelley: What's it to you?

Caroline: I just wondered.

Shelley: Why?

Caroline: She seemed nice.

Shelley: Well don't expect a birthday present from her.

Caroline: I'm not, I just ...

Caroline's confidence drains. She stops talking.

Tony: Ingrid's not here. She doesn't come every day. She sort of pleases herself.

Caroline: Why?

Tony: Dunno, does what she wants. Goes to school if she wants, comes here if she wants. She's no-one's friend really, she just sorts herself out.

Caroline: Oh, I see.

Tony: Didn't expect to see you here again.

Caroline: *(Alarmed)* Why, what's up? Do you want me to go?

Tony: No, it was just Shelley had a go at you last week. I thought you might not bother.

Caroline: But you don't mind me being here? You said ...

Tony: Course not, I know I did. Shelley's not bothered really. She's just a bit awkward sometimes.

Caroline: That's OK then, if you're sure.

Tony: Yeah, it's OK.

Caroline: Only I don't want to go back to school. I'd rather be here *(pause)* if that's OK?

Tony: Yeah, fine.

Caroline: Good. *(Pause)* So what happens now then?

Tony: What?

Caroline: What happens now? What do you do?

Tony: What do you mean?

Caroline: What do you do all day?

Tony: This. *(Pause)* Come to the park, hang about.

Caroline: Is that it?

Tony: Well what do you want?

Caroline: I don't know really. I just thought you might do things.

Tony: Such as what?

Caroline: I don't know really, I just thought ...

Tony: We go down by the canal some days. *(Pause)* Not when it's raining.

Caroline: No. *(There is an awkward silence)* I've got some butties here. *(Gets a package from her bag)* I thought you might all be hungry.

She leaves the bag on the bench. Without invitation, the others, including Shelley, stand and take sandwiches. Caroline has made plenty and they all take at least two.

Piggy: *(Opening a sandwich)* What's on 'em?

Caroline: Ham.

Piggy: *(Stuffing a sandwich in his mouth)* Oh right.

Bazzer: *(To Piggy)* So does that make you a cannibal?

Piggy: *(Talking with his mouth full)* What?

Bazzer: Piggy. *(Pause)* You? ... eating ham? ... cannibal?

Piggy: *(Taking another sandwich)* What?

Bazzer: Never mind.

Shelley: *(Sitting back on the bench)* This isn't ham.

Caroline: Some of them are turkey with lettuce.

Shelley: Oh. *(She starts eating)*

There is a silence as they all eat their sandwiches.

Tony: We go to town some days.

Caroline: What, shopping?

Shelley: Yeah *(Laughs)* sort of.

Caroline: What's funny?

Shelley: Nothing really. *(Pause)* What did you say your name was?

Shelley is looking through Caroline's bag.

Caroline: Caroline. Caroline Dearman.

Shelley: Do you want to come today?

Caroline: Well, yes. Yes if you're going. *(Pause)* Can I have my bag please?

Shelley ignores her and keeps looking.

Shelley: Well, we hadn't planned to but it will be useful having you.

Caroline: Why?

Shelley: They won't recognise you.

Still looking through the bag.

Caroline: What difference does that make?

Bazzer: She means the store detectives. They won't clock you the same.

Caroline: But why would? *(Pause)* Hey now, hang on. You don't go nicking do you?

Shelley: Well they don't give you the stuff.

Caroline: Well, er, no, then. No thanks. I'll stay here with Tony.

During this, she snatches the bag and stands with Tony.

Piggy: *(Still eating)* Tony comes with us. Wimps stay here.

57

Caroline: Well I'll stay on my own then.

Shelley: I told you she was useless. Snotty bitch!

Caroline: I just don't steal things, that's all.

Shelley: Stuck up cow.

Caroline: I'm not criticising you.

Shelley: That's nice of you. *(She gets up to leave. To the others)* Are you lot coming?

Bazzer and Piggy get up and follow Shelley. She stops.

Shelley: Tony?

He hesitates, looks at Caroline then gets up and follows.

Tony: Yeah, I'm coming. See you Caroline.

Caroline: Yeah, see ya.

Piggy darts back and grabs another handful of sandwiches.

Piggy: Ta ra.

Caroline watches them leave as the lights fade to blackout.

Scene 7 — The Park Shelter

It is not long after the previous scene. Caroline is wandering about, picking up the sandwich papers the others have dumped around the place. She screws them into little balls and, using a waste bin for target practice, begins to commentate on and act out a game of darts.

Caroline: *(Imitating a TV commentator's voice)* And haven't these boys done well? Five days of absolutely tremendous darts, edge of the seat stuff, game after game, match after match. Forty eight qualifiers started out on Monday and here we are six days later, one man, three darts and 142 to score for the World Championship. *(Caroline paces up and down as if under pressure. She speaks in hushed tones)* So what's he going to do? He takes a drink from his pint first to collect his thoughts. It's big money these days is darts, no longer a game for the big drinker. Fitness is the byword for today's darts player.

Nowadays, none of them drinks more than ten pints in a game. So, 142 is needed to finish the match and take the championship. Jelly Belly Thompson steps up to the oche. Treble twenty, double sixteen, bull, that's what he'll go for. *(She throws some paper)* That's what he's done. Treble twenty his first dart. Looking now at double sixteen. *(She again throws paper at the bin)* And it's in there, sweet as a nut. So, for a first prize of £50,000, my goodness you can almost touch the tension in the atmosphere, Jelly lines up the bull, *(she throws the paper)* and as if in slow motion, the dart wings its way through the air. It's taking an age to get there, but it's in! £50,000 worth of sheer poetry! Jelly Belly Thompson wins the Municipal Parks Outdoor Darts Championships!

By this time she is jumping up and down and almost shouting her commentary. As she turns, she sees Jake and Jo who are approaching her, completely bemused. She is clearly embarrassed and becomes immediately subdued.

Jake: What you doing?

Caroline: Just ... *(She picks up paper and puts it in the bin)* ... tidying up.

Jo: What you jumping about for?

Caroline: I don't suppose you'd believe I've just won £50,000 in the Municipal Parks Outdoor Darts Championship?

Jake & Jo: What?

Caroline: No, I thought not. *(Pause)* What are you doing here?

Jake: It's dinner time.

Jo: We came to see you.

Caroline: What for?

Jake: Because we're your mates.

Jo: And you should be at school.

Caroline: Yeah, well I'm coming back.

Jo: You keep saying that. When?

Jake: It's been nearly two weeks now. You're bound to get caught.

Caroline: I won't, and anyway, I really am coming back this time.

Jo: Why?

Caroline: I can't win. If I don't come back, you come looking for me, if I say I will, you want a list of reasons written out and delivered to you.

Jo: I didn't mean that. I meant, why now all of a sudden?

Caroline: I just want to. I mean, mostly we have a good time, they're good mates and everything. Ingrid, Ingrid Atherton, she's really nice. But a couple of them aren't my sort so I thought I'd come back.

Jo: When?

Caroline: Next week probably. Let them give out all the assessment forms and then I'll come back.

Jake: So where are they now? The rest of them, where are they now?

Caroline: They've gone to town shopping.

Jake: Shopping? What are they shopping for? *(Realises)* They're on the nick aren't they, shoplifting?

Jo: Are they Caroline? Is that what they're doing?

Caroline: Don't be such a stuck up cow, Jo.

Jake: You're mad Caroline! Stay away from that lot. You'll get a record and everything.

Caroline: Don't be such a wimp. I can look after myself.

Jo: If you go with them, then you're one of them. You'll get done as well.

Caroline: No-one's going to get done. I'm here aren't I? And I'll be back at school next week, I've told you.

Jo: I don't know why you're even bothering with them.

Caroline: And I don't know why you're being so snotty.

Jake: Look, we've got to get back. Are you coming?

Caroline: I've told you, next week. I'll come back then. I'm off down the canal this afternoon.

Jake starts to drift away.

Jo: Just be careful, that's all.

Caroline: I've told you. Stop worrying *(pause)* and keep your mouth shut.

Jo: I will.

Jake: Jo, come on! We'll be late.

Jo: See you.

They exit. Caroline watches them, then she stoops and picks up a ball of paper from the floor. She throws it into the bin.

Caroline: One hundred and eighty.

She exits.

Scene 8 – The Park

The lights stay up from Scene 7. There is a brief pause before Tony, Bazzer and Piggy run on, hard on each other's heels. They are really out of breath and for a moment or two, cannot even speak.

Piggy: He got Shelley.

Tony: I know, I was there.

Bazzer: I said it was stupid, doing such a big place. I knew they'd spot us.

Tony: It was her idea – she wanted the risk. She's mad sometimes.

Piggy: Well she's caught now.

Bazzer: We might all be.

Tony and Piggy look up.

Piggy: Why?

Bazzer: If she talks. They know she was with someone. She might tell them.

Tony: She won't do that.

Piggy: No, it's Shelley we're talking about, not Ingrid. Ingrid might grass.

Tony: Ingrid wouldn't even have come.

Shelley: *(Shouting from offstage)* Coo-ee!

Piggy: What was that?

Shelley: (*Calling again from offstage)* Coo-ee.

They all look.

Tony: It's Shelley.

They leap up and surround her as she appears.

All: How did you get here? / They let you go? / We thought they'd got you. / How did you get away? etc.

Shelley: Calm down boys. *(Pause)* Impressed?

Tony: What happened?

Shelley: I got away. I ran for it.

Tony: Yeah, but when I looked back he had hold of you, just outside the door.

Shelley: I know, but I started crying.

Tony: So he let you go?

Shelley: Not exactly, but it put him off guard.

Bazzer: So what then?

Shelley: I told him who I was, said I was sorry, then first chance I got, I ran for it.

Piggy: Told him who you were?

Shelley: Yes. *(She pretends to be all contrite and tearful)* Oh I'm sorry sir, I'm really sorry sir, my name's Caroline Dearman.

Bazzer: Caroline Dearman? *(Laughs)*

Shelley: I gave him the library card out of my purse.

She waves a purse in the air.

Tony: That's Caroline's.

Piggy: You nicked her purse?

Shelley: When she was giving out the butties.

Piggy: Brilliant.

Shelley: So he reads it. *(Imitates his voice)* 'Caroline Dearman, eh?' *(In her own voice)* Puts it in his pocket. *(In Caroline's voice and pretending to cry)* 'That's right, I've never done anything like this before. My dad will kill me. Those boys ... it was their idea, they made me.' *(Goes to her own voice)* So he says, 'Well I can't help that. You'll have to come with me.'

Piggy: Did he take you to the office then?

Shelley: No, I said, 'I'm not coming anywhere. You should have a lady with you.' That threw him then, so then I said, 'You're hurting me.'

Piggy: This is brilliant.

Tony: Shut up – what happened then?

Shelley: He was all confused. He knew he needed a woman so he started to radio for one and he didn't want to hurt me so he sort of relaxed and when he did that, I was off, straight out of the door.

Bazzer: Fantastic.

Shelley: And all he's got is my name.

Piggy: Caroline Dearman.

They all laugh.

Hey, was there any money in the purse?

Tony: Get lost, it's tight that. Give us the purse.

He takes it.

Bazzer: Get lost Tony *(To Shelley)* Tell us again, Shelley. Do the bit where you start crying.

Shelley: Right, I'm at the door ...

The lights fade to blackout as Shelley recounts her story once again.

Scene 9 – The Park Shelter

The scene is immediately in front of the shelter. This opening is very swift and noisy. Someone – we cannot see who – is on the ground, curled up, trying to protect himself.

Tony, principally, but assisted by Piggy and Bazzer, is kicking at whoever it is, egged on by Shelley. Ingrid is still in the shelter. At first she is placing bags in the hiding place, then she sits as if entirely detached from what is happening. There is a lot of shouting. The scene should appear to be very violent.

Shelley: *(Over the top of the noise)* Kick him Tony, kick him.

Caroline appears, takes a moment to comprehend what is happening then dives in the centre to stop it.

Caroline: Stop it! Stop it! Get off him! What are you doing?

She pushes them back and they obey, except for Bazzer who still wants to have a go.

Stop it! *(Astonished, she sees who is on the floor)* Lowther, it's you!

Lowther wipes blood from his nose and looks up. He clearly doesn't recognise Caroline.

It's me, Caroline *(Pause)* Caroline Dearman. *(Pause)* Your Dek's class at school? *(Pause)* Pancakes!

Lowther finally realises who it is and raises his arm, weakly, in recognition.

Shelley: Do you know him?

Caroline: Yes.

Tony: What did you say then?

Caroline: Yes. *(Pause)* Yes, I know him.

Tony: Before that, what did you say?

Caroline: What? *(Pause)* Oh, nothing.

Tony: You did, you said, 'Pancakes.'

Caroline: What were you doing to him?

Tony: Why did you say 'Pancakes'?

Caroline: *(Annoyed)* It doesn't matter. What were you doing to him?

Jessie enters unnoticed and watches the proceedings.

Piggy: He's a thief.

Big Lowther: I'm not.

Bazzer: *(Lunges at Lowther and kicks him)* Shut it you.

Caroline: Stop it! *(To Tony)* You've hurt him. *(Bends down to Lowther)* What for?

Tony: Piggy told you, he's a thief.

Jessie: And you'd be the one to judge? You and your delightful mates.

Shelley: Oh, just what we need, Mad Jessie. Come to sort it all out, have you?

Jessie: I've come to see no-one else gets hurt.

Shelley: Oo! Get you, Wonderwoman!

Ingrid: *(Stands and steps out of the shelter)* He hasn't nicked anything.

Tony: What?

Ingrid: He hasn't nicked anything, all the gear's there. I looked while you were fighting.

Caroline: *(Standing)* You knew? All the time they were hitting him, you knew he'd not pinched anything?

Ingrid: Yes.

Caroline: Well why didn't you say?

Ingrid: Nothing to do with me, it wasn't my gear.

Caroline: You just watched. What's up with you?

Ingrid: Listen gobshite, there'll be something up with *you* in a minute.

She steps towards Caroline.

Jessie: Oi!

Ingrid looks at Jessie. We see the aggression drain from her.

Ingrid: Come on, we've got our stuff. Let's leave it to Mother Theresa and Wonderwoman.

The gang disperse. Their parting comments are a weak attempt to maintain some dignity.

Bazzer: *(Saluting)* See you then Wonderwoman.

Piggy: Woof! *(Pause)* Woof!

Shelley & Ingrid: Bye *(Pause)* Bye.

Tony: *(Holding out Caroline's purse)* Here.

Caroline: What's that?

Tony: It's your purse. You dropped it the other day, when you gave out the butties.

Caroline: That's where it went! Thanks, thanks a lot.

She starts to open it.

Tony: Don't worry, all the money's there.

Caroline: *(A bit embarrassed she closes the purse)* Course, yes, I never thought ...

Tony: No. *(Pause)* Course not.

The others shout him from offstage.

Got to go.

He turns and runs after the other truants.

Caroline: *(Bending down to Lowther, who is wiping away blood with a tissue which Jessie has given him)* What were you doing Lowther? What happened?

Big Lowther: Nothing. I just went in the shelter and sat on the seat.

Jessie: Is that it?

Big Lowther: The back all fell in. There's a space behind the seat, it was full of bags.

Caroline: I know. They're their bags.

Jessie: *(Bending, offering another handkerchief)* And you were only looking at them?

Big Lowther: They just jumped on me, started kicking. I wasn't going to pinch anything.

Caroline: What were you doing here?

Big Lowther: I just fancied a day off. There's this lad, everyone said he was after me. So I thought a day off would give him a chance to calm down.

Caroline: Why?

Big Lowther: I dunno, they just said he was after me.

Caroline: No, I mean why take a day off?

Big Lowther: Cos I didn't want a pasting.

Jessie: Oh, well, that plan worked then.

Caroline: But I thought you were dead hard.

Big Lowther: *(Wiping blood from his face)* Oh yeah, can't you tell?

Caroline: But there was three of them, they got you by surprise.

Big Lowther: I've never even had a fight.

Caroline: What?

Big Lowther: I'm not dead hard, I don't get into fights. It's just a front.

Caroline: But why? Can't you just be yourself?

Big Lowther: Being yourself's no good. People leave you alone if they think you're hard.

Jessie laughs almost to herself.

Caroline: *(To Jessie)* What's so funny?

Jessie: Nothing really, I was just thinking what a good idea this pretending is.

Caroline: *(To Lowther)* She's right you know. It's done you no good at all has it?

Jessie laughs again.

Caroline: *(A bit annoyed)* So what's wrong now?

Jessie: Well, I was just wondering.

Caroline: What?

Jessie: Whether you were the best one to give out advice. Still, don't mind me. *(Turns and leaves swinging her dog lead)* Ta ra now!

The lights fade to darkness.

Scene 10 — Caroline's House

The lounge is very much like the last time we saw it. Dad is at the table organising some papers, Mum is seated reading. Neither seems particularly concerned when Caroline comes in and whilst they look up, they barely acknowledge her. Caroline, for her part, occupies herself with 'business'. She tos and fros from the room hanging up her coat, getting a drink, changing into slippers etc. until she finally sits in the chair opposite her mother. She has barely settled in her seat when her father – clearly furious – speaks for the first time.

Dad: Where the bloody hell do you think you've been?

Caroline looks to her mother, mouth wide with shock, then back to her father. She doesn't say anything.

Dad: Well, where have you been?

Caroline: School, where do you think I've been?

Dad: That's what I'm trying to find out. *(Pause)* Get up to anything in particular at school?

Caroline: What do you mean, get up to anything?

Dad: Oh, you know, lessons and stuff. What sort of lessons did you do?

Caroline: Well, we had French to start with, I've got some homework for that, then we had double Science with

Miss Murgatroyd, followed by Maths with Mr Hartson, that took us to lunch time so ...

Throughout this speech Dad is nodding and is pointedly paying attention to Caroline.

Mum: Caroline, we've had a phone call.

Dad: Two phone calls.

Mum: And a couple of visitors.

Caroline: *(Trying to seem normal)* Oh, great, who was that then? Anyone interesting?

Mum: Caroline, you've not been going to school, have you?

Caroline: *(Very quietly, looking at the floor)* No.

Dad: *(Forcefully)* Pardon?

Caroline: *(Still looking at the floor)* No, I've not been going to school.

Dad: *(Shouting)* Well where the bloody hell have you been?

Mum: John, please.

Dad: Well, where?

Caroline: The park.

Dad: Is that it?

Caroline: Yes.

Dad: I'm warning you.

Caroline: I've only done it once. Today I've ...

Dad: Don't you lie to me ...

Mum: John, we agreed ...

Dad: Walking in here, bold as brass, you lying, thieving little ...

Caroline: Mum, tell him.

Mum: It's no good Caroline, we know all about it, how long it's gone on, where you've been.

69

Caroline: How? *(Pause)* Who?

Mum: The school's been on the phone, Miss Butterlee. And Jo, she rang as well.

Caroline: Jo? Jo? She promised.

Mum: It's not a promise you should have asked her to make.

Caroline: I said I'd go back. Why couldn't she just keep her mouth shut?

Mum: She was worried.

Dad: She should have spoken out a lot sooner.

Caroline: I told her.

Mum: She was afraid you'd get into trouble.

Dad: She was right there. *(Pause)* We've had the police round here.

Caroline: *(Jumps up, genuinely shocked)* What?

Dad: That's right, the police, broad daylight, large as life. A car outside the house, two policemen inside.

Caroline: *(Worried and puzzled)* But why? What's it got to do with them?

Mum: They've got your library card, Caroline.

Dad: From Furnivals, where you went shoplifting.

Caroline: But I didn't, I ...

Dad: No of course not, weren't you in double Science or something?

Caroline: I never went. I knew they were going, but I never went. *(She suddenly realises)* My purse!

Mum: What about your purse?

Caroline: I must have lost it, not the purse, the card, I must have lost it and someone's found it and then ...

Dad: Can't you stop?

Mum: Caroline ...

Dad: The game's up. All your lying and cheating.

Caroline: I didn't go shoplifting.

Dad: And I don't believe you. Why should I? All the plans we had for you, all the dreams. How could you be so ungrateful? You've thrown it back in our faces.

Mum: We just wanted the best for you Caroline.

Dad: We gave you the best, every opportunity you could have dreamed of ...

Caroline: You just never asked me, that's all.

Dad: We didn't think we needed to ask. What more could you have wanted?

Caroline: I don't know what I wanted.

Mum: *(Crossing to Caroline, putting her hands on her shoulders)* Oh Caroline, what happened to our little girl?

Caroline: *(Pulling away)* Perhaps she never existed.

Dad: Well she's bloody well going to, starting tomorrow. First thing in the morning you're back in school and your mother and I are going with you.

Caroline reacts as if to speak but thinks better of it.

Dad: Now get upstairs and get your books ready, then get down here. I've not finished with you yet.

Caroline exits. Mum and Dad watch her as the lights fade to darkness.

Scene 11 – Miss Butterlee's Office

Seated behind a desk are Miss Butterlee and Mr Hartson. At the other end of the desk is Mrs Ratcliffe and down to her right, completing the crescent shape, are Caroline, her mother and her father.

Miss Butterlee: Well, naturally, we'd like to get this over as quickly and as informally as possible.

Mum & Dad: Of course.

Miss Butterlee: The matter is nevertheless a serious one, both from the school's point of view and from Caroline's. *(Pause)* Still, I'm sure she appreciates that.

Mum and Dad mutter their agreement but Caroline says nothing.

Miss Butterlee: Now, I take it you know everybody, Mr and Mrs Dearman? I'm Miss Butterlee of course, the Head of Year, this is Mrs Ratcliffe, Caroline's form teacher and since the problems appeared to start in Mathematics with the progress tests, I've taken the liberty of inviting Mr Hartson.

Dad: *(Nodding to them)* How do you do? Thank you very much for your time.

Mum: *(A weak smile)* How do you do?

Mum and Dad are clearly embarrassed.

Miss Butterlee: *(Opening a file)* Now what seems to me to be patently obvious from this file is that Caroline is a very capable girl who has come to us with very good reports. *(She looks round the meeting)* Well, no apparent contradictions there. *(Attempts humour)* Not even from Caroline.

There is no response

Yes, well, the mystery is, what on earth made a girl like Caroline behave like this in the first place?

Dad: I think we'd all like to know that.

Miss Butterlee: Well, Caroline, why?

Caroline: *(Very quietly without looking up)* I don't know Miss.

Miss Butterlee: Pardon, Caroline?

Mum: *(Nudging Caroline)* Speak up, Caroline.

Caroline: I don't know, Miss.

Miss Butterlee: Well, perhaps it's the people you were mixing with then.

Dad: I made it clear, Miss Butterlee, that the fun and games of junior school couldn't carry on at Grangemount.

Miss Butterlee: Well, naturally, we expect only the highest standards here.

Mrs Ratcliffe: Standards Caroline was achieving even with the fun and games, if I might say so.

Miss Butterlee: Quite so Mrs Ratcliffe. On the other hand, we've never had truancy from her before, have we? What about the rest of the form group?

Mrs Ratcliffe: They've all settled in very well and early indications are that they're achieving well.

Dad: Apart from Caroline.

Mrs Ratcliffe: That might be true at the moment Mr Dearman, but let's not forget those areas where Caroline has done well.

Mum: Could there be someone influencing her?

Miss Butterlee: There doesn't seem to be at present, certainly not in the form group. What about in the teaching groups Mr Hartson? Has anything come to light in Maths?

Mr Hartson: Well, naturally, there was the incident that I wrote to you about. Reluctance to answer questions, arguments with other pupils and so on. As I said to you at the time, Miss Butterlee, it's a question of attitude. Caroline is not without ability.

Mum: There's a game they play.

Caroline: *(Trying to silence her)* Mum!

Miss Butterlee: What sort of game Mrs Dearman?

Mum: So they don't have to answer questions.

Miss Butterlee: So this was deliberate then Caroline? You set out to avoid answering questions from the start?

Caroline: Not exactly.

Miss Butterlee: Well either you did or you didn't. Which is it?

Mrs Ratcliffe: *(Trying to intervene)* Perhaps Caroline felt unhappy, standing out, when she answered questions. Was that it Caroline?

Caroline: Yes Miss, everyone does. If you answer all the time ·people get fed up with you. They take the mickey, even your friends.

Mr Hartson: Well, that's all very well, but as I said at the time, Maths isn't about making friends. It's about achieving a level of understanding that takes you on to the next stage. I'm not trying to be unfair or unkind but I do pride myself on trying to achieve the very best for all of my pupils.

Dad: Quite right, I've told you before Caroline, you're here to learn. What other people think of you doesn't matter. It's results that count.

Caroline: Everyone does it.

Miss Butterlee: That's hardly an excuse, Caroline.

Caroline: That argument with Dek Lowther.

Mr Hartson: When you threw a book?

Caroline: Yes.

Dad: Precisely.

Caroline: He was making fun of me then.

Miss Butterlee: If it's simply a question that Caroline doesn't get on with people, then perhaps she can move groups, make new friends.

Caroline: *(Panicking)* I don't want to.

Mum: I don't think you're in much of a position to choose.

Caroline: But Mum ...

Mum: It's not up to you.

Dad: Your teachers are giving up a lot of valuable time for you.

Miss Butterlee: And your parents have had to take time off work.

Mrs Ratcliffe: Perhaps it would be a way forward if we devised a scheme to help Caroline back into her classes. Put this behind her. We know she can do the work, perhaps we can arrange for her to copy up work. She could work with me and be reintegrated as she caught up, that way ...

Dad: I don't know, it seems to me that would just be putting off the inevitable.

Mrs Ratcliffe: It's simply a way of getting Caroline back into the learning process.

Miss Butterlee: I can see the point you're making Mr Dearman.

Dad: Caroline's never lacked in ability.

Mrs Ratcliffe: Yes but ...

Dad: Isn't it rather like riding a bike? Fall off, get straight back on. The sooner Caroline gets back in there, the sooner this will be behind her.

Caroline is still looking at the floor. Mrs Ratcliffe looks despondent. Miss Butterlee breaks the silence and concludes the meeting.

Miss Butterlee: Well, if we're all agreed then.

They freeze as the lights fade to blackout.

Scene 12 — Returning to School

This scene is a carousel of different lessons to portray Caroline's return to school. Caroline's class moves around the stage changing position and seating arrangements to indicate the move from room to room. Each lesson has a different teacher and each extract represents a significant moment in Caroline's day. At the end of each scene the performers freeze and a lighting change moves the action to the next 'lesson.'

FRENCH

Teacher: Bonjour mes enfants.

The class all reply, apart from Caroline, who is confused.

Class: Bonjour Monsieur.

Teacher: Right, the moment of truth. Let's see how you got on with that vocabulary you were learning.

The group freeze, pens poised. Caroline sits, unable to do anything.

CHANGE TO GEOGRAPHY

Teacher: Now I want you to take out your books and turn to the maps we did last lesson.

Caroline: *(Looking through a book and asking any one who might help)* What map?

She is ignored because the others are busy.

Teacher: Turn to page nineteen and locate those physical features listed there on your maps.

The class begin working. Caroline is clearly at a loss.

CHANGE TO RE

During the movement Caroline and Jo speak.

Caroline: Where are we now?

Jo: RE. We're working in groups, making a wall display about Palestine.

They enter the 'lesson'.

Teacher: Come on! Hurry up! The materials are all out. Get straight into your groups and carry on from last lesson.

The group is immediately busy and Caroline is left isolated as the other pupils organise themselves.

CHANGE TO MATHEMATICS

Mr Hartson: Right we'll start by going through the homework. Who's got the answer to the first one?

There is a brief pause. No-one answers.

Voice: *(Quietly)* MEWAB

Mr Hartson: I heard that. I want an answer!

The hands go up with the exception of Caroline's.

CHANGE TO SCIENCE

Caroline and Jake talk during the change.

Jake: It's bound to be difficult. You've been *(pause)* away. You can copy mine.

Caroline: No-one's talking to me.

Jake: You'll be OK.

The class line up.

Miss Murgatroyd: I hope you haven't forgotten that today is positively the last day to bring in the field trip replies. If you haven't got it, you'll spend all next Tuesday in the library whilst the rest of us go to the Science Museum.

The class all hold up reply slips with the exception of Caroline.

CHANGE

Caroline exits as the rest of the group go to their lesson. Jo and Jake talk during the change.

Jake: How do I know? One minute she was there then she wasn't.

Jo: Just don't say anything. Look out here comes Nevins.

The lights fade to darkness.

Scene 13 — The Park Playground

Caroline is seated alone. She is in school uniform and looks extremely dejected. After a moment Jessie arrives and sits with her. She doesn't speak, just looks at her. Finally Caroline says something.

Caroline: Hiya, Jessie.

Jessie: *(Pretending to be startled)* Oh! It's alive!

Caroline: *(Not amused)* Very funny.

Jessie: Oh it's like that is it? *(Pause)* I've not seen you for a day or two

Caroline: I went back to school.

Jessie: I hoped you had.

Caroline: It was awful.

Jessie: So you ran away again?

Caroline: Yes.

Jessie: Hardly the answer, is it? So what now?

Caroline: *(Caroline shrugs)* Dunno.

Jessie: I mean they'll know you're missing. They'll be straight on to your parents.

Caroline: I'm probably alright till tomorrow. I only nicked off last lesson. They won't check till morning.

Jessie: Then what?

Caroline: I don't know Jessie.

Jessie: You can't keep running you know, you've got to stop sometime.

Caroline: There's nothing to stop for Jessie. It was bad enough before, but now! *(Pause)* I hadn't a clue what was going on. Everyone was organised. I'd missed everything. Do you know Jessie, no-one even asked why I'd run away in the first place. They just chucked me in at the deep end.

Jessie: Well, you'll just have to try that bit harder. Come at it in a different way. You'll get there.

Caroline: When?

Jessie: I don't know but I know that hanging around the park isn't the answer. *(Pause)* Look, if Jessie's Joy loses tonight, I won't give up. I'll be ...

Caroline: It's tonight? He's running tonight?

Jessie: Of course he is. I told you, a puppy race at St. Helens.

Caroline: I'd forgotten. That's brilliant. Where is he? Is he at the track?

Jessie: No, is he 'eck. He's at the kennels. He doesn't run until 9.30. I'll move him later. I don't want him excited.

Caroline: So where are you off now? Are you going to him? *(Laughs to herself)* Taking him his tea?

Jessie: Don't be daft. *(She shakes her head)* You know nowt, do you?

Caroline: What?

Jessie: You don't feed a dog before a race. They can't run on a full stomach, makes them poorly.

Caroline: I suppose so, obvious really.

Jessie: I'm going home now. Picking up a few things, loading the van, then I'll take him over to the track for about 7.30.

Caroline: Will he win, Jessie?

Jessie: Haven't a clue. Lot of work if he doesn't and twenty quid entry fee gone. But we might win a hundred quid and I shan't be running away, whatever happens. I'll just talk it over at the kennels and we'll take it from there.

Caroline: *(There is a silence as she considers)* Jessie?

Jessie: Yes love?

Caroline: Could I come sometime, to the kennels, to see him?

Jessie: Course you can, anytime. *(Pause)* Outside school hours. You can watch him run if you like.

Caroline: I can't tonight but another time, yeah, that would be brilliant.

Shouting can be heard offstage. Tony and the truants have arrived.

Jessie: Ay up! I'm off. Your mad mates have arrived.

Caroline: They're not really.

Jessie: What mates or mad?

Tony, Bazzer, Piggy, Shelley and Ingrid enter.

Tony: Hello Jessie. Still looking for that dog?

Jessie: *(Deadpan)* That's right, very funny. See you Caroline.

Jessie exits. Caroline starts to leave.

Tony: Hey! Where you going?

Caroline: Home.

Tony: Not good enough for you now then?

Shelley: Never were if you ask me.

Caroline: I just don't want to be late.

Piggy: They checking up on you now then?

Caroline: Yes if you must know. *(Looks at Tony)* Ever since someone told them I was a shoplifter.

Tony: Hey, that wasn't me.

Caroline: Well you had my purse.

Tony: I gave you back your purse but that doesn't mean I did anything else.

Shelley: It was me if you must know. *(Pause)* You going to hit me?

Caroline: You know I'm not.

Ingrid: It was just business that's all, nothing personal. Shelley was caught and needed a way out. You were it. Anyone would have done it.

Caroline: Would they?

Ingrid: Well I would.

Piggy: Shelley did.

They all laugh.

Tony: So what happened? Did you get into big trouble?

Caroline: Over wagging it, not over the shoplifting. The store detective said it wasn't me.

Ingrid: There you are then. You had no worries.

Shelley: You did alright though. I mean you could have grassed on all of us.

Tony: I said you wouldn't.

Caroline: No-one even asked. That's the only reason I said nothing.

Tony: Yeah well anyway. You did alright. *(Pause)* So what now?

Caroline: What do you mean?

Tony: Well are you back with us, wagging it?

Caroline: I don't know ... I ...

Bazzer: Well you're back here now.

Shelley: Wagging it again.

Tony: Your mate Jessie's been missing you.

Piggy: Actually spoke to us yesterday.

Ingrid: Wanted to know where you were.

Caroline: That was nice.

Shelley: *(Mimicking)* That was nice.

Caroline: It was though ...

Bazzer: Get out! She's mad.

Caroline: She's not.

Tony: She's a bit weird, that dog lead and everything.

Caroline: She's not, I've told you. She's got a greyhound, up Thorndike Road, at the kennels. It's running tonight.

Piggy: Get lost.

Caroline: It is. Tonight 9.30 at St. Helens. That's where she went, back home to get ready. *(Pause)* Do you know you can't feed a dog if it's running.

Bazzer: Well it would be hard to keep up.

Caroline: No, stupid. If you feed a dog before a race, they can't run, it makes them ill. Jessie just told me.

Piggy: It probably can't run anyway.

Caroline: I bet it can. I bet it wins tonight. Jessie says ...

Tony: 'Jessie says, Jessie says'. Who cares anyway?

Caroline: Well I do. Jessie says the people who've seen it at the kennels say it'll be a good 'un, a world beater.

Tony: No chance.

Caroline: We'll see. Anyway I'm going now. I've got to get home.

Tony: See you tomorrow?

Caroline: I don't know.

Tony: Well you can't go back to school. You've only been back five minutes and you've wagged it already.

Caroline: I know but ...

Tony: You're better off here. This is where the action is, not stupid school.

Caroline: It's just ...

Tony: There's no choice to make. School's crap. I'll see you tomorrow.

The truants exit. Caroline starts after them then turns and goes the other way. The lights fade to darkness.

Scene 14 — The Park Shelter

The next day. Caroline is sitting on her own at the shelter. Mum arrives. Caroline leaps up.

Caroline: Mum!

Mum: I thought I'd find you here. They phoned from school, said you were missing. They said you'd missed the last lesson yesterday as well.

Caroline: Yes.

Mum: Why Caroline?

Caroline: I don't know.

Mum: You must know. It's you that runs away.

Caroline: It's just ... people pick on me, Mum. My mates let me down.

Mum: Who? Who's let you down?

Caroline: Jo for a start.

Mum: How, how's she done that?

Caroline: She told on me, she told you I was wagging it.

Mum: She did that because she cares. She tried to help you. Jo risked a lot, being called a grass, losing a friend. She did it for you, because she cares.

Caroline: Well I'm not worth it.

Mum: Of course you're worth it.

Caroline: Dad doesn't think so.

Mum: Of course he does. Dad loves you.

Caroline: He's got a funny way of showing it.

Mum: *(Pause)* Come back Caroline, go into school. I've spoken to Mrs Ratcliffe. She's going to work with you, talk things over. You can go back into lessons gradually like she said, Miss Butterlee's agreed.

Caroline: I can't. I can't do it.

Mum: Of course you can do it, you're a bright girl Caroline.

Caroline: It's too hard Mum.

Mum: The best things are never easy.

Caroline: When I come here it's easy. There's no hassle. They don't expect anything.

Mum: And they don't give you anything. What are you so afraid of Caroline?

Caroline: *(Shouting)* You, you and Dad because I can never live up to what you want.

Mum: Oh Caroline, you already have. We love you. We just want our little girl back. The one who smiles.

Caroline: It's too late, Mum.

Mum: You're not even twelve Caroline. How can it be too late? You're not even twelve.

Caroline: Perhaps you should have remembered that when you wanted so much.

She runs away. Mum shouts after her.

Mum: Caroline please, please come back. There's lasagne for tea. It's your favourite. Please come back.

She sinks dejectedly onto the bench as the lights fade to blackout.

Scene 15 — The Park Playground

Caroline is seated alone. She has been crying. Jessie appears.

Jessie: Now then, what's all this about?

Caroline: Nothing Jessie.

Jessie: Who was that lady by the shelter?

Caroline: My mum.

Jessie: Come looking for you?

Caroline: Yes.

Jessie: So you ran away?

Caroline: Yes.

Jessie: *(Pause)* Why don't you just go back Caroline? Look at you, you can't say you're happy. Go back to school then come to the kennels on Saturday, tell me about it.

Caroline: The way you say it, it's nearly a good idea.

Jessie: It is a good idea.

Caroline: I can't, Jessie. I can't face it.

Jessie: You can, you can if you try. You've got mates there haven't you?

Caroline: I've got mates here.

Jessie: Is that what you call them? They're ...

Caroline: Jessie *(pause)* give it a rest and tell me about last night.

Jessie: Nothing much to tell, dog never ran.

Caroline: Why not? What's? ... He's alright isn't he?

Jessie: He is now, no harm done. Someone had fed him. God knows what they'd given him. He was full to bursting, couldn't have run to save his life.

Caroline: Oh Jessie, I'm sorry.

Jessie: Not to worry, he's OK, that's the main thing. At least they didn't hurt him or anything like that.

Caroline: Hurt him. You mean it was deliberate?

Jessie: Oh it was deliberate alright. People get up to all sorts to stop dogs running. It's called nobbling. They do it to fiddle the betting or snatch the prize money.

Caroline: It's just awful, all that work ...

Jessie: It's not wasted. We'll just have to find another race, get him ready for that.

Caroline: Well I think it's awful.

Jessie: Talking of awful ... *(She looks offstage to see the truants arriving)*

Tony, Ingrid, Shelley, Piggy and Bazzer enter.

Tony: *(To Caroline)* Hello, hello, hello. Decided to come then?

Caroline: Yes.

Tony: Good girl. I knew you would. Better than stupid school. Eh Jessie?

Jessie: Well school never did you any good that's for certain.

Tony: Oh very good Jessie, a little joke. *(Turns to the others)* Jessie's made a little joke everybody. *(Pause)* Laugh.

They all feign laughter.

Very good that Jessie, very good. Now then, *(glances at the others)* how did that dog of yours get on then?

Jessie: As a matter of fact, it didn't run.

Tony: *(Building up the moment)* What's that Jessie, didn't run?

Jessie: Someone had fed it.

Tony: Someone had fed it? *(Pause)* But surely ... Weren't you telling us, Caroline, that you shouldn't feed dogs before they run?

Caroline doesn't respond.

> All that planning Jessie, ruined. That's awful. *(Turns to the others)* Isn't it everyone, isn't it awful?

All: *(With obvious insincerity)* Awful, really awful.

Tony: Dear, oh dear, you must be ...

Caroline has crossed to Tony and in mid-sentence slaps him across the face. Everyone is stunned.

Caroline: It was you wasn't it? You did it?

The others start to snigger.

Tony: *(Rubbing his cheek where Caroline has hit him)* So what if it was?

Caroline: You can't bear it can you? You can't bear the thought that someone else might succeed. *(Turns to all of them)* You're not hard you lot, any of you. You're cowards. That's why you don't go to school, you're afraid, afraid of failing. *(Turns back to Tony)* Well you're pathetic the lot of you. I'm going back to school.

Tony: And what will you do when you get there?

Caroline: I'll see my mates. Know what mates are do you?

Tony: Why, do you?

Caroline: Oh yes I've got loads, and one in particular. She's more of a mate than you could ever dream of. *(She turns to leave)* I'll see you Jessie, I'll see you on Saturday.

Jessie: Will you be OK? What about your mum and dad?

Caroline: Oh I'll be alright there. It's lasagne for tea. See you.

She exits. The gang gaze after her. Jessie, who is standing separately, leans towards them.

Jessie: Woof!

The gang, startled, recoils abruptly as the lights go to blackout.

THE END

GOING TO THE DOGS

was first performed at Woolston High School, Warrington, with the following cast

Caroline Dearman	Charlotte Taberham
Mr Dearman	Andrew Brown
Mrs Dearman	Claire French
Jo	Lucy Hodson
Jake	Matthew Clarke
Paula	Bridi Foden
Lucy	Rachel Atherton
Tom	Mike Anderson
Mike	Laurie Stephenson
Lowther	John Geraghty
Tony	John Millman
Shelley	Lindsay Acklam
Piggy	Michelle Bate
Ingrid	Natalie Kelly
Bazzer	Richard Barnes
Jessie	Layna Wood
Miss Butterlee	Holly Fleming
Mrs Marsh	Claire Parker
Mrs Ratcliffe	Stephanie Simm
Mr Hartson	Christopher Kenny
Mrs Wardle	Kate Bailey
Customer	Karen Hanson
The 'Lovers'	Joanne Dobson & Jamie Prosser
Laura	Emma Sherratt
Joanne	Michelle Jones
Karen	Kate McCormack
French Teacher	Alison Bradley
Geography Teacher	Vicki Bradley
RE Teacher	Stacey Williams & Kim Waldron
Miss Murgatroyd	Sarah Burrows
Mrs Nevins	Jessica Buckley-Mellor

Chorus

Beverley Stanley	Sharon Edwards	Claire Dobson
Jenny Roughley	Jayne Fletcher	Zoe Finn
Kelly Fletcher	Rebecca Cartwright	Abbie Murray
Gemma Shaw	Louise Higham	Cassie Fewtrell
Laura Blackburn	Lee Tarry	Rebecca Robinson
Claire Jackson	Claire Woods	Lisa Hogan
Jenny Foster	Jane Wilkinson	Gemma Monks
Nicole Garrity	Yvonne Bentley	Jenny Forrest
Carla Hankey	Jayne Harrison	Amy Barlow
Natasha Laugher	Stacey McCarthy	Eleanor Miller

Stage Crew

Scott Rowland

Kevin Towers

Phillip Littlefair

Gareth Diamond